PROSTATE CANCER, THE MUSICAL!

A Hilarious Tale Of
Invasive Medical Procedures And Self Discovery

(not actually a musical)

Eric Wilson

PROSTATE CANCER, THE MUSICAL!

First edition. January 31, 2023.

ISBN: 979-8215139325

Written by Eric Wilson.

Table of Contents

FORWARD

A musical is a play, where the actors periodically burst into song. Everything is going along normally, and before you know it, somebody is singing at you, all about how they just met a girl named Maria, or how something means "Trouble," with a capital T, and that rhymes with P, and that stands for "pool." Sometimes they sing while they drop a chandelier on the audience.

This thing you're about to read, despite its misleading title, isn't a musical at all. It's not even a play. But it does have many musical references, because that's just a thing my brain does automatically in everyday life. During normal conversation, I will just blurt-sing any lyric reference that somebody accidentally drops into the conversation, because I think it punctuates and adds energy to the situation.

For example, if somebody asks, "Hey who was that detective in the *Perry Mason* TV show," I will not simply answer, "Paul Drake, played by the actor William Hopper." Instead, I will launch into a chorus of "Watching The Detectives," by Elvis Costello. It's clever and fun and not super annoying at all - ask anyone who knows me. In any case, this is weird behavior, especially from a guy who doesn't even like musical theater.

Now, I could have taken this heartwarming comedy-cancer saga and written an actual, proper musical, but do I look like I have that kind of focus and ambition? So instead, you'll have to use your imagination and play all the song references in your head. Don't worry, they're all popular hit songs that have been around for a while, and you've probably heard most of them before. This includes all the chapter headings, plus a few other underlined phrases, sprinkled throughout the book. You can quiz yourself along the way, and see how many you remember.

At the end of the book there is a section called "The Musical! (It's not.)" that lists all the musical references and the songs and artists they came from.

I wonder how many copies this clever, fun, and not super annoying thing will sell. <u>Gonna buy 5 copies for my mother</u>. (There's the first one!)

This book, which is titled as a musical (and is not one), is part factual reporting, part self-indulgent reminiscing, part unsolicited personal advice, and part motivational hogwash. It's a great combination, if you ask me, the self-indulgent author. It's mostly for boys, but girls are also encouraged to give it a look, even if it's just to have a good laugh at our expense. It's written for guys who have just been diagnosed with prostate cancer, guys who have already had it, guys who have never heard of it, and guys who are thinking about maybe getting it. It's especially for guys who have had it, and are prepared, in advance, to roll their eyes and immediately dismiss this whole thing as either an exercise in self-aggrandizement, or a desperate attempt at getting attention and sympathy. You guys will probably enjoy it the most, for all the wrong reasons, and I'm very much in favor of that.

I welcome readers who have no direct personal experience with prostate cancer, but have lost someone to cancer, prostate or otherwise. For you, this book will come across as smartassy and inconsiderate a lot of the time, and I'm very sorry for that. For a lot of us, who are currently in the moment and having the experience in real time, clowning around is our way of dealing with the gravity of the situation. I hope you can get past the disrespectful veneer and find something you like.

Also - and this is important - don't take anything in this book as medical advice. That's why we have doctors, who went to school and learned things, so some uninformed idiot like me doesn't land you in the hospital. I am not qualified in any way to advise you medically, so ignore anything that accidentally looks like me being smart about doctoring. I'm not that smart, trust me.

Finally, it occurs to me that I've accidentally portrayed myself as something of a gritty daredevil here, and that's just not true. I'm a somewhat delicate and introverted goofball in real life, at least when I'm not on stage performing. I really dislike bathroom humor, and I look the other direction when a nurse sticks a needle in my arm, so I'm way out of my comfort zone here. But I've decided to just enjoy my accidental alter-ego and let everybody get the wrong impression.

CELEBRITY FORWARD

I haven't had the time to read this book, but,
y'know, Eric seems like a nice enough guy, so…
I mean, how bad could it be?"

- *"Weird Al" Yankovic*

The author, with the guy who wrote the
Celebrity Forward. As you can see, they have
a relationship that is based on mutual show
business respect and admiration.

ACT ONE

Chapter 1 - Werewolves Of London

Warren Zevon had some reasonably big hit songs. You may remember *Werewolves Of London*, from 1978. It's always popular around Halloween, even these days. The chorus goes, "Ah-hoooo, werewolves of London!" over and over. There are lyrics like, "He's the hairy-handed gent who ran amok in Kent." It's awesome.

Warren dropped dead of cancer (specifically, Mesothelioma) at a relatively young age. I remember seeing him on the *David Letterman Show*, after his diagnosis had become public. Dave asked him about it, and Warren's response was as follows:

"I might have made a tactical error not going to a physician for 20 years."

Me, I had a primary care doctor, a great one. I got connected with her through a Vegas show I was working for, since she was the doctor to the star of this show. But there came a point in her very successful career where she decided to transition to what is known as a "concierge doctor service." This means you, the patient, pay a hefty annual premium to be allowed the privilege of being one of her few, select patients, and then you pay for doctor visits on top of that. I did not have the kind of disposable income to finance such an arrangement, so I did not sign up for my membership in the exclusive club. And then I just sort of forgot to get a replacement doctor for 15 years.

It's a very popular thing, prostate cancer. One out of eight guys get it, lots of guys survive it. As you probably know, the trick is to catch it early, then your chances of beating it are really good. That's all predicated on having some basic common sense about seeing doctors. Many guys are able to do that. Warren Zevon and me...not so much.

I've always looked a little younger than my years, and I've always felt generally great. That just means that, when I drop dead at a normal age, people will be slightly surprised. "He seemed so young. Huh. I wonder what's on Netflix." That's how I imagine the reaction to my eventual demise. And when I look in the mirror, I think, "Do I need to see a doctor? Nope, I look good."

I also have the maturity level of a 14-year-old. I work in show biz, running audio for events in Las Vegas. I run a lot of corporate events, and when you see me strolling around Las Vegas convention venues in my suit and tie, meeting with clients and using professional grownup vocabulary, you'd think I must have completed my college degree in the usual four years, instead of twenty. When I'm not getting paid to pretend that I'm a grownup, I play music in bands, I perform in plays and burlesque shows, and I do not hang around sensible people as much as I probably should. This is not a set of circumstances conducive for behaving responsibly, especially when it comes to the seeing of doctors. I would go to doctors whenever something bad happened to me, and in the words of Danny Elfman, world famous movie score composer and former leader of the band Oingo Boingo, "Nothing bad ever happens to me."

Don't misunderstand me, I'm not completely irresponsible. In my defense, I did get a colonoscopy (five years later than I was supposed to), which I totally aced. I've never smoked (unless you count the half dozen cigarettes I pretended to smoke in high school), I've never drank (unless you count the couple dozen drinks I tried while in college), and

I've never tried any recreational drug...not even weed. When everybody else in my peer group was out getting hammered on weekends, I was at home in my bedroom, practicing guitar and trying to learn Eric Clapton songs. I don't eat much red meat, I don't put salt on my food, and for the past 60+ years I have been reasonably active. Well, not sedentary, anyway. Why, just this morning I came down the stairs, then went running right back up to retrieve my reading glasses. That puts me on par with Olympic athletes, pretty near.

I am also a tiny bit delusional when it comes to my state of health, you might notice. On the plus side, I'm also very self-aware, so that counts for something.

So anyway, there I was, at 60+ years old. A spring in my step, a glint in my eye, and feeling mighty proud of myself for looking so young and dashing, and not having ailments. I had every reason to believe I would live to be 100. A-hoooo, werewolves of London!

Chapter 2 - Sign, Sign, Everywhere A Sign

I had started noticing that going to pee was feeling a little different than usual. It crept up on me gradually, and a lot of you guys will find this part really familiar. Once in a while, there would be a little bit of a hesitation before the waterworks would commence. This would typically happen if I'd been holding it for a few hours, like on a drive from Vegas to Disneyland. This is a drive that I do every couple of months (remember - maturity level of a 14-year-old). Upon arrival in Anaheim, after parking in the garage and taking the tram to Downtown Disney, I'd saunter into the park and hit the restroom by City Hall. And there would be a little hesitation. No big deal.

I had also begun having the typical old guy problem of getting up in the night to go wee at least once, sometimes twice. This had gone on for a couple of years...again, starting sporadically, not happening all the time. This experience was compounded by the fact that I'm frequently guilty of eating and drinking right before bedtime, which is what all smart people say you should not do. But I am Rock and Roll to the core, so I scoff at dietary advice from smart people. Besides, I figured it was no big deal, just like the hesitation thing.

Now, when somebody starts a sentence with "Besides, I figured," it often means one of two things. One, they were completely wrong about something, and/or two, an unexpected and unpleasant consequence followed. So, stay tuned for one or both of those things.

4

The very gradual and sporadic progression of this experience evolved into that feeling of not being finished. Prostate guys, you know what I'm talking about. For the rest of you, it goes like this: you go to yonder restroom. You do your thing. The event finishes up. And you think, "Huh. Feels like I'm not really finished." But nothing is coming out, even if you push and squeeze. So, you must be finished, despite that odd feeling that you're not. Then, 15 minutes later, you have to go again, urgently. What the hell? You can still easily hold it for 4 hours on the Disneyland drive, even while consuming a Venti Coffee Frappuccino on the way. Why do you need to go again, even though you just went 15 minutes ago?

As I said, this evolution doesn't happen overnight. And in the beginning, the symptoms don't even happen every day. More like once a week. So, you conveniently brush it aside, and you might even think, "Maybe it'll get better on its own." Besides, I reminded myself, despite my youthful glow, I was now over 60 years old, and old guys typically start having perfectly harmless mild peeing difficulty, due to perfectly harmless conditions, commonly found in perfectly healthy old guys. It's very common, I tell you. It's just BPH. That stands for Benign Prostate Hyperplasia, which is the fancy name of a perfectly harmless enlarged prostate, which is...perfectly harmless. No big deal. There are pills available. Not that I needed them yet.

It reached a tipping point for me one day when I was running audio for a typical corporate event at the Venetian, here in Vegas. This was one of those events that always involves a steady stream of presenters coming up onstage, talking about how great the company is, about how we all have to do even better next year than we did this year, and by the way, now it's time for the awards ceremony. Everything is "phenomenal," and the sales team is "crushing it," and we're "monetizing the analytics" like never before. No matter who the client is, it's the same exact content every time. This is the kind of event I always run, day in and day out,

at various Las Vegas hotel convention centers. I love these events, for
real. They are the least Rock and Roll type show ever, and yet they
invariably include an 80s themed corporate schmooze party, and all the
corporate attendees show up awkwardly costumed in rented neon leg
warmers, rainbow Mohawk wigs, and zipper-encrusted jackets. There
are angular, pointy sunglasses available at the table where you check in.
Ken from Marketing chooses the red ones.

But this was the businesslike portion of the event, with the presenters
and the monetizing. The client group had just come back from a break,
and I had just made a trip to the men's room. Ten minutes into the
next presentation (featuring Ken from Marketing), I called my audio
assistant over, told him to mind the mixing console, and informed him
that I would be back in sixty seconds. I scuttled out of the ballroom
in a barely-disguised panic, and made a beeline down the opulent and
shimmering Venetian hallway to the gent's room, where I pushed and
squeezed extra hard.

Being a sound guy at the Venetian. You can tell by my expression that I was desperately thinking about running to the men's room. Again.

Chapter 3 - Somebody Get Me A Doctor

Okay, it reached a tipping point, but this had to happen three times, at three different events, before I finally got on the Inter-Googles and started hunting for a urologist. Because I live in Vegas, which is not exactly a bastion of high tech or medical cutting edge, I was scrupulously vetting my choices. I mean, had any of these bozos actually graduated from med school? And if they had, did they graduate last in their class? Why else would they be practicing in Vegas? Somebody has to graduate at the bottom of the class, you know, and they still get a degree.

Mind you, if you want a boob job or a face full of Botox, there are loads of places here that'll fix you right up with top quality results. Surgery tourists, as they are known, sometimes make Vegas a destination choice for cosmetic work. They arrive with gaunt faces and droopy parts, and leave with a decidedly "inflated" overall appearance and renewed self-esteem. A producer friend of mine, who is a legend in her field, and happens to be Jewish, once said to me, "A lotta new faces in temple yesterday. A lotta new faces on old bodies."

But you don't really hear about people traveling to Vegas for an angioplasty or neurosurgery. Those people are more likely to zip off to Cedars-Sinai or the Mayo Clinic. As for me, I eventually settled on a guy who seemed to have the least number of horrifying Yelp reviews, and made an appointment.

I must digress here for a moment. Since my first real doctor search, I've learned a thing or two about doctor selection. Remember, I'm kind of late to this game. The main thing I've learned is this - nearly all of the terrible reviews you read about a doctor have nothing to do with the doctor. They have to do mostly with the front office staff, and secondarily, the billing department.

There will always be a certain number of patients who walk into a medical facility with a breathtaking sense of entitlement, and want to treat the place like it's a hotel or restaurant. And they get mighty crabby if the front office doesn't wait on them as if they were a visiting Kardashian. Yes, it's true that some people have a genuinely bad experience at the hands of a careless receptionist or secretary, and I don't mean to marginalize their bad experience. But reading doctor reviews has told me a lot more about the patients than it has about the doctors.

Along the same lines, as soon as someone has a problem with the billing department, that seems to be their cue to unleash a seething condemnation of the medical staff...who, by the way, have nothing whatsoever to do with billing. While some deadbeat is waxing prosaic about how they were unfairly turned over to collection, the medical staff is busy prolonging people's lives and enduring verbal abuse from patients who can't bear to sit in a waiting room for ten minutes longer than expected. I don't know why complaints about a billing department are even allowed on doctor review sites.

Believe me, I personally know what it's like to get a bill for $23,000, even though your insurance absolutely does cover that thing you had done. It turns into a nine-month fight with your incompetent insurance company, taking many unexpected twists and turns, until you're exhausted from the fight. If you're lucky, somebody from the medical facility where you had the thing done finally steps in, acting in the capacity of a "fixer," and fixes the problem for you, sometimes by covert means that are definitely against company policy. Thank goodness for those people who advocate for patients, because we patients don't stand a chance against an insurance company's corporate policy. But none of this has anything to do with the doctors or their associated medical people.

Anyway, my advice to you, dear readers, is to ignore how many Yelp stars a doctor's office has, and carefully read the bad reviews. If they seem to indicate that the actual doctor is an unfeeling bastard who would rather be on the golf course, by all means reject that guy. If all the complaints are about the rude girl at the front desk, ignore them. Rude Girl isn't providing your medical care, the doctor is. Rude Girl's favorite band probably just broke up. Give her some space. She's in grief.

Chapter 4 - Doctor Please, Some More Of These

I arrived at my new urologist's office with one goal: get the pills. Because I was totally fine, and I just needed some harmless special pills for my harmless and minor peeing difficulty, which did not even happen every day, so no big deal. I knew about the pills mostly because guys would tell me about them, in men's rooms. It's the weirdest thing. Multiple times, some random stranger has decided to tell me all about his pee-enhancement pills in some random restroom. I have no idea why this is. Do they feel the need to share their joy with every other guy they encounter? Is it like, "Hey, as long as we're both in here going wee, let me tell you all about my medical condition?" Do I have the kind of face that says, "Please tell me all about how, since getting the pills, you now pee like a two-year-old?" Because that's exactly what one of these random dudes told me. "Now I pee like a two-year-old."

The "pee like a two-year-old" guy had accosted me in a Starbucks restroom, near Olympia, Washington. He was probably the third guy who had started up this conversation with me, in such a location. This was several years before my own adventure started, and I was surprised and bewildered at the sudden new direction my restroom experience had taken. Why is it socially okay to say this thing to a guy you've never met before, and who you have just encountered for the first time in a public men's room?

I've decided that there's an invisible camaraderie between all dudes which weirdly manifests itself while they are going wee next to a stranger. It's a situation in which the storyteller feels oddly safe. You, the recipient of his story, are temporarily trapped as you conduct your process, but you are also guaranteed to be gone from his life forever as soon as one of you exits the men's room. So, he assails you with the thing he so desperately needs to say out loud, and that thing is, "I'm okay now! I'm not gonna die! Isn't that great?"

Maybe he can't tell his Mrs. or his real friends, for some reason, maybe because they will not disappear into forgotten memory five seconds after they leave his side. Sometimes it's hard to share an experience like that with those you know and love. Or maybe he has already told those he knows and loves, more times than they care to hear, and now he has to tell everybody else in the world, and the men's room is the sanctioned place for the sharing of such information. Also, he can tell you because you're a fellow dude, and fellow dudes have this shared context. The fact that you're a complete stranger makes it even easier. You will listen to him for fifteen seconds, then you will evaporate. You're a transient men's room psychiatrist, working for free. Congratulations on your new career. Even if you graduated at the bottom of the class.

Anyway, irrespective of this outpouring of euphoria in public men's rooms, I was on a mission to get myself some of these pills, that I didn't really need, but hey, why not? After all, it's Vegas.

However, as I had suspected, I also got The Finger.

Chapter 5 - Gonna Use My Fingers

The Finger is no big deal, but to some guys it is A Very Big Deal. The Finger crushes their soul, and touches them in a way that gives them confusing feelings. I get it, I understand and sympathize. It's unpleasant and uncomfortable, and do the lights really have to be so bright in here? Also, the hot physician's assistant, whom I smiled at out in the hallway, doesn't know this is happening, does she? Because if she does, that is going to produce deep psychological scarring that will last a lifetime, and I'm not prepared for that. You know what, on second thought, I feel better. Maybe I don't need the pills after all. Put that rubber glove away. I'll just run along now.

Shut up and embrace The Finger! The Finger is here to sort you out! The Finger probes, and it knows things! All hail The Mighty Finger!

Honestly, it's kind of remarkable, the kind of information that a qualified medical professional can learn with an index finger in the right location. I'm seriously impressed. Anyway, you're going to get the finger, so you might as well get used to the idea. Start by mentally removing the capital letters, like I just did in that last sentence. It's just a routine digital-rectal exam, and it takes about 10 seconds. Don't make it into something humiliating or shameful, and for reals don't make it into some sort of test of your latent homosexuality. If you find the experience genuinely mortifying and horrible, okay, fair enough. You're in the majority. If you are surprised that you actually kind of liked it, well, hooray and extra bonus, I guess. Maybe you knew in advance that you would kind of like it, and that's perfectly okay too, if that's your thing.

If you are mortified and ashamed that you actually kind of liked it, and are subsequently plunged into depression, I'm not qualified to help you through that. I encourage you to talk to someone who is good at these things. Me, I approached the finger as a medical exam that I definitely didn't like, but I sure didn't attach any non-medical baggage to it. It's not so bad, fellas. Besides, there were greater horrors yet to come.

I secured a prescription for the pills, all according to my master plan. The prostate pills do not shrink an enlarged prostate - there is no medication that will do that. Rather, it is a very targeted muscle relaxer that aims itself at the troublesome prostate and makes it release its enlarged iron grip on your urethra, thereby allowing improved peeing. And it worked just fine. Not a day-and-night dramatic difference, but a noticeable effect after just a few days. I wasn't "peeing like a two-year-old," but I didn't have that "not finished" feeling anymore. I was completely fine with taking these things for the rest of my life. All the way to 100.

I had left my first urologist visit with a follow-up appointment for two weeks later. This was long enough for the helpful pills to become well established in my system, and I arrived for my follow-up only to be greeted with another episode of the finger. This time it was not administered by my new doctor, but by a new-new doctor. I had just barely gotten to know my new doctor, and now there was some other dude about to give me the finger. People have such carefree attitudes in this office. Anyway, in he goes, has a quick feel, and announces that "the right side feels firm."

My first thought was, "Well, the left side had better get off its lazy ass and hit the gym." The right side feels firm? What does that even mean?

I got the distinct impression that it was not firm in a good way. I was pretty sure the right side was supposed to be squishy soft like the left side, and furthermore, the right side was here to cause trouble. Was there a way to un-firm the right side? Another pill, perhaps? A special potion? Testing was in order.

Chapter 6 - Check Baby, Check Baby, 1, 2, 3, 4...

I was ordered to go get a PSA test. PSA stands for Prostate Specific Antigen. What's an antigen? It's a molecule, or a set of molecules, that can bind with antibodies and T-cell receptors. They can trigger immune responses and cause all sorts of excitement, and you're capable of churning out all sorts of these things. Antigen, by the way, is a shortened version of the phrase "antibody generator." Anti + gen.

When some disrespectful molecule comes snooping around your innards, it's time to cook up some antigens. Antigens come in various different flavors, depending on the type of disrespectful molecule that needs to get slapped around. Your immune system is always on the lookout for signs of molecule delinquency, and is ready at a moment's notice to fling some flavor-appropriate antibodies at any snot-nosed punk molecules who deserve it. I mean, just look at them with their long hair and unkempt covalent bonds...electrons jumping around, willy-nilly...

Even if there are no signs of trouble, your prostate likes to throw some of these antigens around, just on general principles. You know, just to let everybody know who's in charge down here. Just a small show of force. Nothing too dramatic. Just in case anybody gets any crazy ideas about disrespecting the prostate. The older you get, the more your prostate throws this stuff around. "Get off my lawn!" he yells, at any passing molecule that looks his direction. The neighborhood molecules all laugh at the old prostate, and he shakes his puny fist at them. The old prostate is basically Clint Eastwood, and not sexy young Clint from High Plains Drifter. More like bitter, curmudgeonly Clint from Gran Torino.

Testing for prostate specific antigen makes a pretty decent measurement for the likelihood of prostate cancer. It's not a sure thing, because your PSA can read high for a few different reasons. After all, sometimes a high PSA level is caused by an enlarged prostate that is perfectly benign and doesn't want to cause any ruckus at all. Sometimes.

I was sent off to one of those street corner medical labs to have a PSA blood draw. You see these places popping up all over town, like food trucks. In addition to drug testing for job compliance, with urine and hair samples, they also suck blood out of you and test it for various problems. They might also make delicious tacos in the back, but I don't know this to be absolutely true. This is a simple process (the blood draw, not the taco production) that takes about ten seconds. And it produces a rather useful piece of information.

A normal PSA level for someone whose age is between 40 and 49 should be from zero to 2.4. If you're between 50 and 59, your PSA should be from zero to 3.6. If you're between 60 and 69, your PSA should be from zero to 4.5. If you're between 70 and 79, your PSA should be from zero to 5.2.

Mine was 33.

Wait! Wait! Do-overs! Do-overs!

See, there was a technicality. A little caveat that nobody told me about. A mitigating factor that skewed the test results. This is going to take some explaining.

My urologist is great, and so is the staff. But they are not exactly generous with unsolicited information. I'm not sure why that is. Maybe it's because they have a zillion patients to see every day, and they don't have time to deliver a comprehensive cancer tutorial to every single one of us. Maybe they figure we're all going to go snooping on the Inter-Googles anyway and learn for ourselves. To his credit, my doctor always asks at the end of an exam, "Do you have any questions?" I always have some, and I always remember them on the drive home, but never while I'm sitting there in front of him.

So, it turns out that ejaculation will give you a higher PSA reading. It turns out that you're not supposed to "get your cookies" for at least 24 hours before a PSA blood draw, and some places say 48 hours. And I just happened to learn this interesting fact while snooping on the computer at home, a few days after my PSA results were sent to my doctor's office.

Now, I have always considered myself to be an avid enthusiast of orgasms. Whether with cooperation and participation from someone else, or just on my own, it's been a favorite lifelong hobby. I pride myself in having refined my methods to high standards, and never fail to produce very satisfactory results, if I do say so. So I called my urologist's office and got one of the very nice front office gals on the phone, and I explained that, contrary to industry recommended standards, the time between my PSA blood draw and the last time I "got my cookies" was, in fact, six hours.

And should I go get another PSA test?

She shakes her head in disbelief (I assume), sighs deeply (I'm guessing), and puts me on hold for a minute, to check with the doctor. She comes back and says yes, go get another test. So I go back to the street corner lab/taco truck a week later, this time having had nothing but pure thoughts for 48 hours. And I get a second PSA test.

It was 29.

Okay, so there's that. Now, as I mentioned, your PSA number is not an actual measurement of cancer, but as leading indicators go, things did not look so good. There are any number of harmless reasons for a PSA level to be a little high, but 33 (okay, 29) is not "a little high." It's not the highest ever, by a long shot, but it was enough to get everyone's attention, especially mine. In light of this surprising accomplishment on my part, further testing was in order. And when I say "further testing," I mean a fairly unpleasant in-office procedure known as a prostate biopsy.

Strap in. It's gonna get bumpy.

Chapter 7 - You Let Me Violate You

Remember back when some of you were dismayed about The Finger? That's adorable. Allow me to spin the rollicking tale of the prostate biopsy, a procedure that we will gently characterize as "rather invasive." I arrived at my urologist's office ready to face the music, knowing in general terms what was going to happen. But really, it's the little details that enhance and magnify the experience, turning it into something extra special.

A prostate biopsy involves taking twelve (12) tissue samples from your prostate. "Wait a minute," you might be thinking, "Samples? From an internal organ? And this is done in a doctor's office? Not in a large, well-equipped hospital with state-of-the-art machinery and copious amounts of anesthesia?"

That's right, champion, right there in a little tiny exam room. The same room where you got the finger. Only this time, things are gonna get real. Realer than the finger, by a lot. First of all, despite the rather invasive and moderately violent nature of this procedure, there will be no comforting anesthesia of any kind - at least there wasn't in my case. You'll be vividly awake and crisply alert. Second of all, there will be no comforting application of pain killer. Oh, there's a pain killer, but its application is anything but comforting. Third of all, there's going to be a special guest involved, who will make the whole experience just a little bit more memorable. More about that in a minute.

Picture it: you arrive in the little exam room. The lighting is not any more romantic than last time - it is once again the cold glare of the fluorescent overhead. The hot young physician's assistant gal, whom you smiled at in the hallway on your first visit, comes in and informs you that she's going to shoot your backside full of antibiotics, in preparation for the aftermath of this thrill ride. So you drop your stylish cargo shorts with a classy flourish, because you have reluctantly come to terms with the fact that you will never look "Rico Suave" to the HPA (hot physician's assistant) after this, and you get what feels like a quart of antibiotic concoction jabbed into your well-lit ass. The HPA leaves, so you may reflect on the day's events, so far. "Well, so far, I guess this isn't so bad," you decide.

The doctor comes in carrying some sort of medieval torture contraption. I didn't get a good look at it at the time, but it featured video surveillance capability, a multi-gizmoed probe appendage, some rubbery arms or possibly hoses, and most likely a small nuclear reactor for power. In my brief glance, it reminded me of a miniature version of Doc Octopus from the Spider-Man comic, additionally fitted with that stabby thing that gets slowly thrusted at Han Solo's face when he's in the Imperial torture chair ("They didn't even ask me any questions..."). I was instructed to lie on the exam table, on my side, with my knees pulled up.

And here we must pause for a moment and bask in the radiant glow of the best moment of the prostate biopsy experience. One of the things I did not know going into this exam was what position I would be assuming. I had wondered if it would be the gynecology exam position, with feet in stirrups. But no, it was the less mortifying, on-the-side, fetal position. I was so happy. And at least the HPA wasn't going to be in the room to witness...

Hang on...

Hold up...

She's...still...here.

The HPA was still in the room. Because she was going to be minding the video surveillance part of the contraption, while the doctor operated all the levers and hoses and stabby things. Great. Just great. This is the "special guest" I mentioned earlier. I was glad I had opted to keep my Disneyland baseball hat on. You know, so I could still look cool while undergoing the thrill ride.

Anyway, in goes the probe. Not that it matters that much, but in case you are wondering: no, the probe is not soft and lifelike, with realistic texture, and shipped to you in a discreet, unmarked brown package. It is rigid and unyielding, actually, and it definitely does not buy you a drink first. Anyway, the first order of business is to deliver four (4) shots of painkiller to the four quadrants of the prostate. No problem, it's right there within easy reach. Just on the other side of the rectal canal. So, you know, we have to stab through that to get at the target, and then stab through it a bunch more times to get the samples. Hence the need for the giant dose of antibiotics. I got four stabs of "pain killer" from Mini Imperial Doc Octopus, and I was quite surprised and fascinated to observe just how many nerve endings one has up in there. But I'm sure the pain killer was at least partially effective, based on what happened next.

What happened next was a series of samples, twelve of them, as you might recall. Out of those twelve, about a third of them did not have a sting, and only a few of them had a major sting. The painkiller must have missed those spots, or maybe it fully kicked in sometime later that evening. With each sample, there was a loud noise and percussive impact, very similar to a nail gun. I was going to count them, but it was such a whirlwind of excitement and sensations, I lost count after two. I remember wondering if my Disney hat was going to stay on. I half expected it to get blown across the room, cartoon style, every time the nuclear-powered nail gun was discharged. My doctor was rather talkative while doing this procedure, and I was grateful for it. I said so afterward. It really helped distract me from the intensity of the process. Pretty soon he said, "Okay, two more to go," and I was surprised and pleased at that bit of news.

Out comes the probe, and the HPA quietly leaves the room, allowing me to preserve the enormous amount of dignity I still had left. Doctor says to me, "Well, that's probably the worst thing that's ever been done to you."

I thought for a moment, and told him it was "the least amount of fun I've ever had, per minute." It's a relatively short procedure, but boy howdy, it's action packed. He told me I did great, which is probably what he tells every stunned patient, right afterward. I decided to take it as a genuine compliment, because sometimes a metaphorical pat on the head is just what you need. I was instructed to go ahead and take my time getting dressed, to take as long as I needed. That's because the experience can leave you a bit light-headed and in a mild state of shock. I quickly collected my wits, then I got dressed and slowly floated out to my car like a week-old helium balloon. I decided then and there to have my prostate removed on general principles, just so I would never have to have this procedure again.

But don't worry - you'll be fine...

Chapter 8 - I Got The News

A few days after the biopsy themed attraction, the pathology report was sent to my doctor's office, and I got the office manager to email me a copy. Of the twelve (12) samples taken, the number of them that came back as testing positive for cancer was: twelve (12). Three of the samples also showed nerve invasion. This was not great news, but I had assumed it wasn't going to be, based on my PSA number and the unauthorized firmness of the right side. Up until this point, there had been no clinically tested, positive conclusion that I definitely had cancer, and now there was. On top of that, there was the matter of the Gleason score.

The Gleason score, sadly, is not a test of your trivia knowledge all about Jackie Gleason, star and creator of *The Honeymooners* TV show from the 50s, and featured character (Sheriff Buford T. Justice) in *Smokey and the Bandit*. No, the Gleason score is a number that is derived from lots of data taken from all twelve of the biopsy samples, and it categorizes how aggressive your cancer is. My Gleason score was pretty high. Not the absolute top, but right up there. Like 8 point something, for you experienced guys who are keeping track of this stuff.

I had frittered away my time, being cavalier about my peeing difficulty, and now here I was, a bona fide cancer patient. My doctor told me I'd probably had it for a couple of years. Ah-hoooo, werewolves of London...

There was still an important choice to make - whether to remove the offending prostate or not. With twelve (12) positive samples, there was no point in removing part of it or getting the radioactive seeds installed. That's a procedure where they insert one hundred little radioactive pellets right into the part of your prostate that's cancer-y, and then you have to scrub the toilet after every single time you use it, plus you have to not stand near pregnant women for a few months. I'm serious. I know a guy who had it done. Anyway, that was out of the question, because there wasn't anything viable to save. The whole thing was a useless lump, and it had to come out. Maybe.

There was still the question of whether the cancer had spread hither and yon, to surrounding areas. Or maybe even non-surrounding areas. That's the thing about cancer. No matter where it starts, it might go all the way to the other end of you, if it feels like it. You can have lung cancer, for example, have your lung removed, then have the same cancer show up later, in your brain, and it's still called lung cancer. If mine had spread, there wasn't much point in removing my prostate, because that would not solve the problem. Radiation and chemo and hormones might solve it, at least for a while. But we needed more information.

I was scheduled for surgery preemptively, just in case it had not spread. That was Plan A. Plan B would be radiation and whatever other therapies were deemed necessary, rather than surgery. My doctor had said, "If it's spread, I don't want to put you through all that pain." And I thought, that's good. Because, as Carly Simon so eloquently put it, "I haven't got time for the pain." I had a ticking time bomb in there, and we needed to move fast. They got me the soonest possible surgery date in whatever hospital had an open slot. I was also sent scurrying off to a radiology lab to get two more tests done. We knew I was cancer-y, now we needed to know where all it was located.

Chapter 9 - Come Up To The Lab And See What's On The Slab

A few days later, I arrived at the radiology lab for my CT scan, with low expectations. Between the PSA number (29, not 33!), the biopsy (12 out of 12!), and the Gleason score (*Smokey and the Bandit!*) I thought there was a pretty high likelihood that my prostate had flung cancer cells all over the place, in an angry snit, because the neighborhood molecules wouldn't get off his lawn.

I met the nice kids who were running the CT lab, and I hopped up onto the moving table that runs you into the scanner. One of the kids stuck an IV line in my arm, because in this procedure they push a contrast dye into your vein, to help the scanner produce an image.

While they were getting things ready, the line popped out of my arm. Just sort of fell out, and laid there. The youthful technician who had put it in looked at it quizzically and said, "Oh." Apologies were made, and the nice youth stuck the needle back in, this time with a little bit more tape. I wondered if this was a bad sign. I also wondered if this was the team that normally makes tacos in the back, and they were having a go at radiology for the first time.

The kids all cleared out of the room, in preparation for the scan to begin. They were in the control room, pressing whatever buttons needed to be pressed, getting ready to send me into the tube. And...

The line pops out of my arm. Again. Only this time, the contrast dye is already under pressure. So the line is now thrashing around like a garden hose on a hot summer day, spraying everywhere, but mostly all over me. I take a big quantity to the face, it's all in my hair, all over my shirt, and I yell the following:

"UM...! YOU GUYS...!"

The youthful technicians all come running out, all four of them. And they panic. One of them is wrestling with the spurting contrast dye line as it flails about, one of them is attempting to mop off my face, which is now soaked with special medical juice that was supposed to go in my vein, and I'm pretty sure one of them is hastily re-watching the YouTube instructional video on how to stick an IV line into a patient. The fourth one, I assume, is looking over the classified ads for "Lab Technician Wanted," as she peels the ineffective tape off my arm.

I keep my lips and eyes pressed tightly closed, since I'm not sure if a person is supposed to ingest this goop. After frantically rushing around the scene of destruction, they finally settle down long enough to ask me if I might like to abandon the procedure for today and come back another time, please. I think they are secretly planning on not being at work on the day I might come back. Also, I'm pretty sure one of them now has an interview lined up at a delicious taco truck.

My urologist's office has gone to great efforts to get me into this scan ASAP. There's no way I'm leaving and coming back another time. We have a deadline to hit, and the results of this scan will determine whether or not I keep my surgery date. I say no, I will not be leaving, let's sort this out and get it done. One of the youths decides he'll stick the line in my other arm, since the first one is cursed, or something. As he's jamming the needle into my vein, he seems to be hitting some sort of barrier in there. He hollers something about a valve, and the needle won't go any farther. I wonder how far from the bottom of the class he graduated. The panic level in the room is ramping up again. He finally decides he's going to try sticking the needle in the back of my hand. That seems to go okay. He yells, in a very hyper-excited manner, in a heavy Russian accent, "I'll put a lot of tape! Like ten times around!"

Well, he only does two wraps of tape, but it seems to do the trick. The line stays in, I get slid into the tube multiple times on the moving slab, and apparently everything goes like it should. Although, in all the excitement, nobody has given me any instructional talk, and I notice, after the procedure is finished, that there's a little sign located up at the top of the machine. This is a sign you can't actually see from your position of lying on the table. I guess you're supposed to read and comprehend it before you lie down. But it says you're supposed to hold your breath and be very still when you're in certain positions inside the tube. I have been very still, but I have not held my breath. I leave the place wondering if the resulting imagery will look like a blurry Polaroid from 1975.

The next day I had to go back. My urologist's office had managed to get me into the CT scan tube at short notice, and they did the same with the bone scan appointment, which was the other test I had to get. But the bone scan lab wasn't available on the same day as the CT lab, so I had to go back.

The bone scan lab was a one-woman show, run by a very nice and very competent gal who, unlike Elite CT Scan Team #1, had graduated from lab technician school well before three weeks ago, and (I assume) considerably nearer to the top of the class. She was great. She did the radioactive dye injection herself, which went perfectly. Then I had to go away and occupy myself for a few hours as the radioactive sauce coursed its way through my bloodstream, like James Bond's martini. When I went back that afternoon for the bone scan, it was relaxing and calm, not shaken, not stirred, and it provided some balance in my overall experience. The chaos and mayhem of the CT scan were effectively offset by the professionalism and serenity of the bone scan. All I had to do now was go home and wait for results, which were already being processed. Even as I was climbing off the table and getting my shoes back on, the nice bone scan lady said there was already a person working on uploading the data. The results from that lab would be at my doctor's office the next morning, at the very latest. Who knows what was happening with my data over in the CT madhouse...

Chapter 10 - The Waiting Is The Hardest Part

Knowledge is power, so they say. During the couple of days after my CT and bone scans, while waiting for life altering news, I spent some time on the Inter-Googles, reading and researching all about prostate cancer surgery, radiation, chemo, hormone therapy, and whatever else people were presenting as treatment options. I learned a lot of numbers and statistics, percentages and chances. I looked at charts that showed how many years a person typically lives if they have my PSA level and Gleason score, and none of them had me destined to live to 100, by a wide margin. I waited for lab results. But I was determined not to be surprised or unprepared for any eventuality, so I read and learned and tried to squeeze some power out of knowledge.

In this situation, you also start planning your European vacation. You want that sooner, rather than later, I think. Otherwise, it becomes less of a vacation and more of a death march. Despite all this, I remember being pretty chipper and pragmatic, I guess because that's the sort of flippant, yet Pollyanna-like fellow I am in general. Heavily consequential turns of events don't faze me much, and I'm pretty comfortable with mortality. Still, I did look up some statistical data about how often someone dies during the actual procedure. It was a figure low enough to satisfy my sense of probability and odds, so that was fine.

I have faced death a couple of times before, under completely surprising and unexpected circumstances. A long time ago, when I was 21 years old, bulletproof, and playing in a touring rock and roll band, I was nearly murdered with my own guitar. It's a great story, one that I will not tell here in its entirety. But as I opened my eyes while lying face down on the floor of a Montana bar, I saw the would-be murderer walking slowly towards me with a large, jagged piece of my Gibson Explorer. He had already smashed me over the head with it three times, knocking me unconscious with the first impact. He had broken it to bits on the floor as I lay unconscious, and was now returning to the spot where I lay prostrate (not prostate!) to finish the job. I had regained consciousness, but I couldn't move yet. And I remember thinking, as I watched him approach me, dramatically back-lit as a silhouette, "Well, I guess this is it. I haven't lived a full life, but I guess this is how it ends."

I survived that incident. And now I was over 60 years old and had lived through many other wild adventures, and getting smashed on the head with my own guitar was only one brief example. Checking out of this mortal coil at 60-something was not my plan, but it could have been worse. The guitar murderer could have dispatched me at 21, yet here I was, having another in a continuing series of exhilarating experiences. So I waited for lab results, played my guitars and drums and keyboards, did yard work, cleaned the pool, went to Starbucks like nothing was wrong, and wondered how much it cost for a hotel room near Disneyland Paris.

1982. Twenty four years old and bulletproof.

Chapter 11 - Hangin' On The Telephone

One morning, a couple of days after the radiology lab adventure, my phone rang. It was the surgery scheduler from my urologist's office, telling me that we were keeping my surgery date. Midway through her sentence, I interrupted, saying, "Hang on, you mean my CT and bone scans came back negative?!"

I was very surprised. It was the happiest phone call of my life. We were back to Plan A. Never mind radiation and all that other business, the "Devil Inside" was getting sliced right out! And good riddance! CT and bone scans all clear, I'll be damned. As an added bonus, they had managed to secure a surgery date at the good hospital - the fanciest one in Vegas. Apparently, my doctor's office was keeping on top of changing developments, and a date opened up there. I felt my chances of survival tick up by at least half a percentage point.

There is a load of data supporting the notion that the success rate of major surgery is directly tied to how big the city is, in which the hospital is located. You stand a noticeably better chance of survival in a big metropolitan hospital than you do in a small-town facility. And Vegas is kind of an overgrown small town in many ways. There are well over two million people here, but Nevada is consistently either dead last in the nation, or second to dead last, when it comes to education, for example. The fancy hospital is the most "big city" type of any of the local places, and I was all in favor of any extra edge I could grab.

I went back to my urologist for a briefing on the procedure, and to collect various paraphernalia for surgery preparation. I had never had major surgery, never stayed overnight in a hospital...well, not as a patient. This was new territory for me, and I was quite looking forward to it, in a weird way. I think it was a little bit like getting ready for your first summer camp, another activity I somehow never participated in, so I can only assume. I had my doubts about the accuracy of the scan results, but the conclusion was not just based on the breathtaking incompetence of Elite CT Scan Team #1, it was also based on the conclusion drawn from data obtained by the very qualified bone scan operator. So, I reasoned that, between the two, it was probably okay.

One of the things I had to get done before the big day was a preliminary once-over exam at the hospital, which included a covid test. This was in the Summer of 2020, there were no vaccines yet, and hospitals were being very scrupulous about controlling the plague. The technician giving the covid tests was sequestered in a tiny "clean room," with seriously comprehensive air scrubbers roaring away, giant ventilation hoses running everywhere, and plastic sheet coverings on every piece of apparatus. It looked like the sinister hose and ventilation works you see in the scary sci-fi movies, except brightly lit in the non-romantic, fluorescent style of a prostate biopsy exam room. The tester wore multiple masks and face shields, a sealed lab coat, and an air of desperation. She seemed like she had been sentenced to shovel toxic waste until one of her hapless patients accidentally transmitted covid and killed her. The tension was palpable. But I escaped the clean room and passed the covid test, along with the battery of other exams, so I was allowed to keep my surgery date.

I spent the remaining days before my operation reflecting on the situation, and coming to the irrational and amusing conclusion that my favorite hobby was trying to kill me. I don't know how many women are reading this - as I mentioned, it's kind of a boys' book. But trust me when I tell you - and the other fellas will back me up on this - having a penis is loads of fun. It's packed full of nerve endings and, well, you womenfolk have a similar bundle of nerves in the same location, after all. So you know about the stimulation feature. But the boy version also launches special boy fluids like a bazooka, which is pretty entertaining. And I was going to have that feature deactivated. Oh, I'd still be able to "get my cookies," in a way, after some recovery. There would be a period where things would be completely non-functional for a while, then I could work my way back up to orgasms one day. But there would be no more launching of special fluids to entertain and delight passers-by.

This was totally fine with me. It's devastating for some guys, especially if they don't feel like they've done everything they wanted to do with that function. But I'd had plenty of fluid-based adventures in my time, and I was completely okay with losing that feature, especially if the tradeoff was not dying of cancer. That seems like a really easy choice.

And so it was that, on the night before my operation, without fanfare, on my own, and encouraged by a selected example of video entertainment, I spurted my last spurt. "Well, that's the end of that," I thought. And I looked happily forward to a medically prolonged lifespan.

Chapter 12 - Cuts Like A Knife

Oh boy, robotically assisted radical prostatectomy! Robots! Radical! Yeah!

Robotically assisted radical prostatectomy means that, instead of slicing you open from stem to stern, like in the olden days, they make five small incisions at five locations across your tummy. The one in the center, just above your belly button, is where the camera goes in. The other four are for the robot arms (which, incidentally, is the name of the apartment building, "Robot Arms," where Bender and Fry live, in the TV cartoon *Futurama*). The "radical" part means that the whole prostate is coming out, not just a part of it. The way I see it, if you're going to have this operation, you might as well be rad.

The surgeon operates the robot arms while looking at the camera image. The robot arms do all the slicing and pulling and twisting and whatever else goes on in there. For all I know, the robot arms collect all the sliced bits into a Zip-Lock baggie, crab-walk across the floor, and toss it in the trash for you. The robot arms probably high-five each other while they look around inside you to see if there's anything valuable worth stealing. After all, they've just carried out a successful hit on Clint Eastwood in there. They feel like the Corleone family, from *The Godfather*. They're full of themselves, drunk on power, and ready to threaten the townsfolk, plus maybe put a horse's head in somebody's bed.

No, that's not true at all, none of it. The robot arms are benevolent and friendly. I, for one, welcome our new Robot Arm Overlords, with open...arms.

There's a light on the robot camera arm, so the surgeon can peer around in there and spot any unauthorized cancer bits that need to be forcibly evicted. I keep forgetting to ask if there's a video recording of the procedure. I bet there is. I might want to show it as a party feature.

On July 13, 2020, I arrived at the plush hospital, dressed comfortably, excessively self-scrubbed multiple times with special hospital-issued disinfectant products, my innards aggressively flushed out from the flushing-out drink I had drunk the night before, and carrying minimal possessions. I was dropped off at the waiting room and left to wait on my own, which is how I wanted it. This was for the same reason I told almost nobody that I had cancer in the first place - I didn't want to have to take care of everybody. They all mean well, but you're left having to reassure people, hear them express their heartfelt concern, and generally host a therapy session to make them feel better about your situation. I'll just sit here by myself, thanks.

I enjoyed hanging out in the enormous, expansive waiting room, checking out the other patients and their companions, wondering what they were in for. Every so often, a nurse would come fetch a patient into the back hallway, sending them on their way to their procedure. The rest of us browsed our phones, murmured with companions, or wandered around, sometimes gazing out the floor-to-ceiling windows at the immaculate hospital landscaping. Calming background music played on the overhead speakers. I thought about how amusing it would be to have *Raining Blood* by Slayer suddenly erupt out of the music system.

Despite missteps like the one at the CT scan lab, I'm a fan of the medical profession, and I think it's pretty great that idiots like me, who know essentially nothing at all about how to remove an organ or install a gizmo inside a human without killing them, are allowed to avail ourselves of such expertise. It's a really good arrangement for us, the general public. I mean, you can drive your car for a while with a badly functioning fuel injector, putting off the repair until you can afford it, or until you can be without your car for a couple of days. You can drive it around with a smashed-in fender for a year, until you finally decide to get it fixed. But if one of your important internal squishy bits gets a disease or otherwise stops working properly, you need someone with a much higher skill level to dive in there and fix you up right away, without killing you.

It occurs to me that doctors get a lower amount of appreciation than car mechanics. I see so many people complain about their health care providers, about how the operation didn't turn out with optimum results, or how they had to wait a longer time for service than what they were promised. They distrust medical advice, they read some spurious article and become self-appointed experts, and they deride professional credentials. The general public seems to resent the medical profession for being overpaid, for being smart, for being elitist, and for not snapping to attention in a manner that pleases the patient. Look all over social media and count how many times anybody praises their doctor. And I'm not talking about veterinarians. Vets routinely get praise for restoring kitty and puppy to health. But not human doctors. Meanwhile, Bro goes on and on about Awesome Dude at the car fixit shop, because Awesome Dude got Bro's car back on the road, and it's better than ever, and while we're at it, how about a shout out to Other Awesome Dude at the window tinting place, he's awesome!

Car mechanics are seen as saviors, doctors are seen as servants. Uppity servants, at that.

By and by, I was called back into the inner sanctum of the hospital. They fixed me up with a high-tech hospital bed, suitable for stylish lounging, as well as wheeling through back hallways. I traded my street clothes for a chic hospital ensemble - a flowing gown with matching hat and sock-booties. I got stuck in with the IV. And then came the best part. I was pretty comfy in my little spot, but the blanket was making me a bit warm. As I fussed with it, a passing nurse asked me if I wanted the air conditioning attached to the gown. Whaaat?! Are you kidding? An air-conditioned hospital gown? Heck yes! She connected a hose to a special orifice on the gown, and I was instantly breezed and refreshed. It was amazing. Like a wearable version of the air-conditioned seats in high-end cars. I had so much fun playing with the air-conditioned gown, I was almost disappointed when my doctor showed up for the pre-surgery talk.

My urologist was also my surgeon, and I suppose he was also ostensibly my oncologist. That's handy, because a lot of responsibility is concentrated in one guy, which makes for a very straightforward dynamic. There was never any "I'll check with the other person," he was all of the persons. He gave me a rundown on what was going to happen, and asked me if I had any questions. As always, I did have, but I would not remember to ask them until after the whole event was over. Anyway, I assured him I was all good, and let's do the thing.

Next, the anesthesiologist came in and introduced himself. I liked him, though I was a little dismayed that he was wearing his mask below his nose. Remember, this was deep in covid times, pre-vaccines, and I thought maybe an anesthesiologist, who was consulting with a patient, in an actual hospital, might want to be a little more observant of mask protocol. I told myself that he'd probably have it on properly during the operation. He explained how, as soon as I arrived in the operating theater, he would immediately push the happy juice into my IV, the magical chemical compound that instantly erases all anxiety and turns the world into an idyllic paradise. Friends of mine have had this happy chemical in their hospital stays, and they say it's really something. That sounded good, although I didn't feel like I was going to need it. I already had a pretty cheerful outlook. After all, highly skilled people, who were not car mechanics, were going to repair me.

The anesthesiologist left, presumably to meet up with the surgeon and decide what interesting variations on prostate surgery they might like to try that day. Meanwhile, I had a little more time to enjoy the fabulous air-conditioned gown and shoot a brief selfie video for future social media use. Then a guy from hospital security came in to collect my stuff. Despite the perfectly clear instructions on one of the many pre-surgery documents I had been issued, I had forgotten to empty all the cash out of my wallet before coming to the hospital, so I asked him if he could count it and sign something. Well, that was normal protocol anyway, so no worries there. He assured me that my gear would be completely safe, and that it would be appearing in my room promptly after the procedure, and off he went.

We were counting down to the big show, and I was getting kind of excited. Not scared, I hasten to point out. Excited. I simultaneously felt a pleasant sense of calm about the whole thing. Maybe that's because I'm too stupid to realize I'm in danger, like the frog in the boiling water. Maybe I'm deer-like, and the headlights make me stop in my tracks and not think. But I relaxed in the light of the oncoming truck, and thought about what sort of funny monolog I might perform for the surgical team.

Chapter 13 - It's Showtime! Showtime!

The time had come to journey to the operating room. I had prepared my hilarious remarks, my personal possessions were secured, and I really wished I still had my phone so I could take video of me making my grand entrance. After all, I was going to be devastatingly funny. The friendly nurse disconnected me from the air-conditioned gown feature, and I was sad about that. But off we went, through the hospital's back hallways. I was surprised how unceremonious that trip was. I'm in the back-of-house hallways in Vegas casinos all the time, and this was exactly the same. Gray linoleum floors, and those 2X6 wood rails along the walls, so carts full of equipment can bang into them and not punch holes. Basic, industrial fluorescent ceiling lighting - well, they're probably all LED now. Supplies piled along the walls (underneath signs that say Do Not Store Anything Here), a vaguely industrial feel to the whole area, narrow corners to navigate, and big rattly freight elevators. Less glamorous than I had imagined. I felt like a bin of cleaning supplies being wheeled to the employee dining room for a spill cleanup.

As we made our way along the route to the surgery venue, I wondered if we might collide with an oncoming cart full of overpriced snacks, or a battalion of black-suited banquet servers, but then I remembered we weren't actually in back-of-house at a Las Vegas hotel. Traffic was light. I chatted away happily with the nurse, who probably wheels two dozen patients along that route every day. It took a minute for her to warm up, and I think that's because most patients are quiet and contemplative as they are wheeled to their fate. She probably wanted to be respectful of the typical patient stress. Me, I'm too stupid to be contemplative in this setting, so once I had demonstrated that I was oblivious to the magnitude of the situation, we had a nice, though brief, social time. Good conversation, good skill at navigating, smooth piloting of the bed. I give this Lyft driver high marks. Since my wallet had been confiscated, I couldn't offer a tip.

Eventually we arrived at the operating room. The ceiling was very high; it looked like there might have been gallery space up above for student observation. It was a much bigger room than I had expected. They could have had five radical prostatectomies going on in there, all at once, with a beverage cart coming around, and trays of hors d'oeuvres served by radical robot stilt walkers. Not cozy at all, very grand and imposing, actually. There were some big fancy machines stored along one wall, and I was reminded of the Monty Python sketch where the doctors are talking about the machine that goes "ping!" and how they should get the most expensive machine going, in case the hospital administrator comes in. I had about five seconds to take this all in before my wheeled bed was turned around and parked alongside the operating table.

I announced, with an airy gesture and impeccable comic timing, that I was here for my Botox treatment, and I hoped everybody else was also here for that procedure. There was some sort of reaction, which I remember as appreciative of my clever humor, but which might actually have involved some eye rolling at the "comedian" who had just been wheeled in. They asked me to scootch myself off of the rolling hospital bed and onto the operating table, which I did, carefully arranging my stylish hospital gown in the process. Once situated, I wondered when the surgeon and the anesthesiologist were going to show up, and if the "happy juice" was going to start anytime soon.

And then I woke up in recovery.

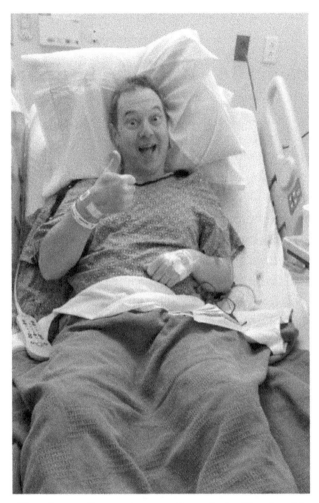

Three hours after coming out of anesthesia. The cheerful
expression is due to industrial-grade medication.

Chapter 14 - Wake Up, Little Suzy

I don't actually remember waking up, of course. A lot of you have had this experience, where you come out of anesthesia and your first memory has you already sitting up in bed, in mid-sentence. I've had two experiences like this before, once in college when I had my wisdom teeth out, and once when I had my colonoscopy. I remember thinking, "Hey, wait a second, what happened two seconds ago? Like, what was the first part of this sentence I'm currently saying?" A few disjointed fragments of conversation with hospital staff and a few memory blackouts later, I was installed in my proper hospital room. Only then did I take stock of my condition.

For starters, the Las Vegas doctor people didn't accidentally amputate anything I was supposed to keep, so that was good. I seemed to be more or less a functioning human, but of course I had various tubes and contraptions attached to me. The five stab wounds didn't look super awful, and one of them was now being used for my abdominal drain tube. The other four were glued shut with some kind of medical super glue.

Oh, here's an amusing side note - I have a belly ring. Because there's nothing sexier and more stylish than a 60-something-year-old dude with a belly ring. Hey, don't judge me! I had purple hair in 1980, I got my first (and only) tattoo in 1997, and I got a belly ring in my early 50s! You don't know me! Anyway, it's not actually a ring, it's a curved bar. You know, with the little ball ends, one of which screws onto the bar after you've inserted it. So, I had, of course, removed all jewelry in preparation for getting sliced and stabbed. But the center incision was done right above the belly button, and it looked like the site of my decorative jewelry was pretty well ruined. Oh well, another small price to pay, I decided.

I was pleased with myself for not dying on the operating table, and I felt better than I thought I would. No doubt that was mainly due to the high quality, hospital grade medication in my IV. And looking over my incisions, I thought something like, "Well, this is okay. I'll be right as rain in a couple of weeks." Nobody had said anything about the operation not being a complete success, so I assumed it had been. I had a very nice convalescence in my private room, in the fancy Vegas hospital. A lot of other guys have it much less cushy during their recovery. My maternal grandfather had his prostate out in the 1950s, and he had to go back to work two days after.

Oh, the catheter. I should probably get around to talking about that. Well, I knew there was going to be one installed, and sure enough, there it was. I looked at that thing and knew we were mortal enemies, but I also knew I needed it to get through the next nine days, so I decided to not make it mad. We eyed each other warily and agreed on a cessation of hostilities before any hostilities had begun. But I did that hand gesture where you make a V out of your fingers, point them at your own eyes, then point them at the enemy.

The hospital staff were completely great. It was as if they had outfitted the place with Starbucks baristas - the happy, positive kind, not the bitter, resentful kind. The kind who are also in nursing school, like the ones at my usual Starbucks. I had resolved in advance to be the ideal patient, to help offset the cranky bastards they must have to deal with, day after day. I promised myself I would never ring for a nurse, and I surprised more than one of the crew by asking if there was anything I could do to help them. Try that some time, it's pretty fun. They look at you as if you're insane, but they leave your room smiling.

Chapter 15 - Get Up, Stand Up

After some adequately delicious, mostly liquid hospital cuisine, I undertook to begin my self-guided physical therapy. They want you up and walking around right away, because it helps prevent blood clots and strokes. And who wants to keel over dead from a stroke, after having made it through a robotically assisted radical prostatectomy? That would take away all the sense of accomplishment. So, a few hours after waking up in recovery and getting my bearings, I completed 20 trips from my bed over to the door of my room, and back. It's harder than you think it'll be. You look at the distance between your bed and the door, and it seems so much more significant than it should. You remind yourself that actual doctors want you to do this thing, so that probably means it isn't completely dangerous and crazy at all, despite it seeming a bit dangerous and crazy. You basically feel okay, all things considered, but at the same time you also feel like your insides have been in a knife fight with a New York City street gang, and lost. The best word I can think of to sum up the sensation is "fragile." Not only are you walking on eggshells, you are a 200-pound eggshell yourself. All your movements are done very slowly and very carefully, with heightened awareness. I can't imagine what it must be like for people who have had real, no-kidding major surgery, like a kidney transplant or a quadruple bypass. I was a rank amateur by comparison.

On every trip to the door and back, I would pass the bathroom and think, "Ha. I won't be needing that, will I?" You know, because of the enemy catheter and the fact that what little food I currently contained was nowhere near exiting anytime soon. I felt like I should get a discount on my hospital room. After all, I was not going to be utilizing all of the features. But I guess it's like "resort fees" at Vegas hotels. You have to pay for all the amenities whether you use them or not - amenities like Wi-Fi that runs at dial-up speed, and a gym that's closed for remodeling. I guess it could be worse. You could have to pay for things a la carte, as needed. Like on that budget airline, whose name slightly resembles "Spurt," the one that charges you extra for a carry-on item, a seat belt, oxygen...

After completing my trips to the door and back, I settled back into my hospital bed, with all its contraptions and containers of liquids. And it was here that I embraced my favorite feature of my room. As if the experience of the air-conditioned gown wasn't enough to make me giddy, my daytime nurse dude hooked me up with the leg squeezers. Oh, they are lovely. They're not complicated, they're just air-filled contraptions that strap onto your lower legs with Velcro. They inflate every couple of minutes or so, and kind of pulse a bit, and it was like a day at a resort. Maybe you've seen those high-fangled $10,000 massage chairs on display at the state fair, or the somewhat lesser versions installed in airports. We have them set up at Vegas conventions sometimes. They squeeze your arms and squeeze your legs and do complicated things to your back and neck. The leg squeezers are like those, except just the lower leg part. My dear old mom finds them distracting whenever she's in the hospital, where she has been many times, but I love them. And I wondered if the other Vegas hospitals had them. Well, I had 'em, right here in the fancy place. I had pneumatic leg squeezers, I had free soft hospital food, I had a good internet connection, and hospital security had returned my phone without stealing anything out of my wallet. I felt like I was like staying at the Bellagio. Apparently having a lump of cancer removed improves your optimism and cheerfulness...and warps your sense of luxury.

Chapter 16 - Day After Day

The next morning, I decided to do my laps. I was told that, if I felt up to it, I could walk around the floor, by which I mean the entire 5th floor of the hospital wing. So I detached the beloved leg squeezers, released all the clips securing my assortment of tubes to the side of the bed, grabbed my IV tree, and gingerly shuffled out into the hallway. I don't know exactly how far it is around the floor, but I did three laps. Again, harder than you think it's going to be. And slower.

On my second lap I passed a woman, about my age, headed in the opposite direction. She was also dragging her IV tree, and was similarly outfitted in the standard-issue hospital livery. We exchanged a brief greeting, and shared "that look" with each other. That's the look that says, "This sucks," "I'm kicking ass and so are you," "Hell yeah, we're beating this thing," and "You're awesome," all at once. It's the kind of instant camaraderie that's generated by a shared experience, which needs no explanation or details. We were both shuffling around the floor, doing our laps, executing an act of defiance against immobility, blood clots, and anything else that was thinking about getting in our way. <u>Ain't nothin' gonna break-a my stride, ain't nothin' gonna slow me down</u>. We've got laps to do, at a slow pace, and with very careful movements. So, everybody make way for champions.

I decided that completing three laps was a pretty good accomplishment, so I returned to my room, parked the IV tree, reattached all the hoses to the bed frame, very carefully installed myself back in the bed, and reunited with my beloved leg squeezers. I felt great. I would have lost an arm-wrestling match with a kitten, but that didn't matter. I had gotten myself out of bed, performed all the nuts and bolts with the hospital appliances, lumbered three eggshell-treading laps around the floor, redid all the appliances, and stuck myself back in bed, all without getting help from the staff. Mission accomplished. I'd be back playing guitar and lifting speaker cabinets in no time.

My operation had been done in late afternoon, and about 26 hours later I was released from the hospital. Everything had gone great, so it makes sense that the last medical task would go haywire. I know what you're thinking - some kind of catheter weirdness, right? No, that bit of custom fitted plumbing was operating as it should. But a certain other device didn't want the party to end.

My daytime nurse dude disconnected the catheter hose from the hanging setup on the IV tree and installed the portable collector that straps to your leg. I thought, "Only nine days, only nine days, only nine days..." He also disconnected the IV line from the back of my left hand - the same location where Elite CT Scan Team #1 had finally achieved success. That all went fine.

The trouble happened when it came time to remove my abdominal drain. After surgery that happens anywhere between your chest and your pelvis, they often install a drain hose to collect any residual blood and whatever other fluids that might be seeping inside of you. And after a day or two, or three, or whatever is called for in your particular situation, it gets removed. And your own body just absorbs any little leftover spare fluid as best it can, until the internal seepage stops. In my case, after one day of drain hose, it was time to get the thing out of me.

Only it didn't want to come out. My daytime nurse dude, who was completely great at all times, gave it a gentle pull, then a stronger tug, then several pro wrestling maneuvers. It did not feel pleasant. It felt downright uncomfortable to have a hose stuck in my side, with an increasingly distressed nurse trying to yank it loose. He was really sorry, and felt really bad. I can't be mad about it - he was such a great attendant in all other capacities.

He called in another nurse to give it a try. She had the same lack of success, but happily, did not persist with the violent pulling for quite as long as he did. I grimaced and tried to breathe. They were both really sorry.

Then they tracked down a third nurse, who was reported to be the undisputed queen of drain hose removal. The Serena Williams of her craft. A force to be reckoned with. Meanwhile, I was seriously considering wearing the drain hose as a permanent fashion accessory, rather than endure another violent attempt at removal.

"Oh, who are you wearing this evening?"

"Oh, this? It's the new Drain Hose, from Hospital Supply Closet Couture."

"Ah, such a bold choice!"

<explosion of paparazzi flashes>

Drain Hose Queen sashayed into the room, and announced with an imperious flourish, "Oh yeah, I pull these out of spines all the time."

It was a claim that was simultaneously reassuring and alarming. Questions popped into my head. Were the patients unconscious when these spectacular removals were performed? Did the patients have to be heavily sedated, either before or after this remarkable stunt? Did they live to tell the tale? But she gave that thing a deft twist and out it came, without so much as a whimper. The three of them then conferred about the finer points of abdominal drain removal and the style of the twisting movement, and I couldn't help but wonder if maybe this topic should have been covered sometime during medical school.

Anyway, thanks to Serena, Slayer of Hoses, I was mercifully free of the abdominal drain tether, and it was time to gather up my stuff and conclude my first ever hospital stay. I changed out of my stylish gown and sock-booties, and back into my standard wardrobe of cargo shorts and a cartoon t-shirt. I took a farewell photo of the leg squeezers and bade them a tearful goodbye. And I went home.

-INTERMISSION-

Have a snack. Discuss with your friends.
Talk about how you don't usually like musicals, but
this one is pretty good. Make plans to catch a Broadway
show someday, maybe Book Of Mormon or Hamilton.
Wander out to the lobby, check out the merchandise
table. Maybe buy a t-shirt or a fridge magnet, or
something. Hum one of the tunes from the first act.

Okay, intermission's over.
Imagine *Werewolves Of London* is playing again…

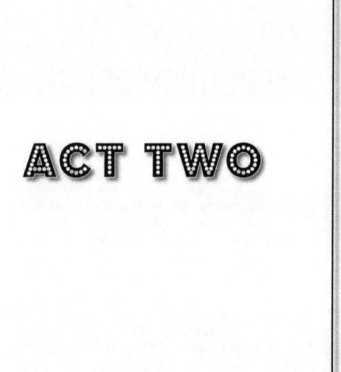

Chapter 17 - Homeward Bound

I didn't get a visit from my urologist/surgeon in my hospital recovery room, and I didn't hear from the office for nine days, which was when my post-surgery follow-up was scheduled. That was fine with me. I didn't care to hear about how the operation went, and I didn't care to know about any unexpected surprises that might have been discovered in there. For all I knew, everything had gone perfectly, and I was cured, and all I had to do was concentrate on recovering. Don't bother me with details.

There are several goals you want to achieve in the recovery process, and the first one is to just exist in a somewhat normal home situation. You want to evaluate how much of your daily routine you can perform without danger or discomfort, and try to get on with life. Before I went in for the operation, I had asked my doctor's office if I was going to be able to negotiate stairs afterwards. I needed to know if I had to set up a bed situation on the ground floor. They told me I probably didn't want to be going up and down the stairs all day long, but a couple of times a day should be okay. And it was. I geezered my way up and down the stairs without incident, grasping the banister firmly, advancing one step at a time, moving like a traditional zombie in a George Romero film.

Like all surgery patients, I cautiously reentered the world of normal food. You don't feel like eating very much at first, and that might be partly due to the residual effects of the high-powered hospital meds, which have not fully worn off. So, I did not go to my favorite all-you-can-eat sushi place, nor did I consume most of a large take-out pizza from my usual middle-of-the-night pizza depot, in one sitting. I think what happened is I ate like a normal human should eat. I mentioned to a friend of mine that I had lost ten pounds as a result of the whole process. He said, "Don't worry - you'll find 'em." And of course, he was right, as of about 8 weeks later. Oh, I had all good intentions of turning over a new leaf and maintaining my newly svelte proportions and showgirl figure, and maybe even making efforts to go further toward my ideal weight goal. Ha-ha! That's hilarious! I eased my way back into casual gluttony, vowing to one day mend my ways. I vow that a lot.

I also discovered I had a numb spot. My left groin area had no surface feeling. This is pretty traditional for surgery patients. When the robot arms go marauding around inside you, hacking their way through the organs and tissues like a band of stainless steel swashbucklers, it's fairly common to have a little nerve damage as a result. Ghost Clint was running for his life, and a certain number of civilian casualties are to be expected, while chasing down the fugitive. It's like that opening scene from *Team America - World Police*, the puppet-action movie from the *South Park* guys. You know, where they chase down some criminal and accidentally lay waste to the entire city of Paris in the process. Then they casually announce to all the shocked and appalled French locals, "*Bonjour!* Everything is *bon!*" Anyway, I know a guy who has a bit of a numb foot, as a result of some lower back surgery. Team America was causing mayhem in there, while they were fixing his backbone. And like him, I considered it a perfectly acceptable side effect.

Just home, the day after surgery, with a few of the guitars.
This is as straight as I could stand up. Medication still in effect.

Chapter 18 - Gimme Three Steps

The day after I got home, I was out in the front yard, inspecting the grounds. It was a beautiful day, in the Las Vegas version of "beautiful day," in July. That means it was clear blue sky and probably only about 115 degrees outside. This is what keeps the entire country from moving here, as they yearn for our relatively cheap real estate and complete absence of blizzard conditions that you typically find in the Upper Midwest. They come here, endure the blistering summer Vegas weather for 5 days of vacation, and run away screaming. Like I say, it was a beautiful day.

In the weeks running up to my operation, I had been digging enormous amounts of stray grass out of a flower bed near the front of the house. It was a big job, and involved daily scrutiny, as I was constantly attacking new sprouts that grew up from bits of the root system that was still lurking down there. Before surgery, I had the whole area under control. But now there were a few intrepid shoots starting to poke through. They knew I was incapacitated. They saw their chance.

I started thinking about how walking was perfectly allowable, as was stair climbing. I mean, they had me up and walking a few hours after surgery. What would be the big deal...now, follow me on this...what would be the big deal if I just took a perfectly normal step forward, but with my foot coming to rest on the edge of a shovel? I mean, that's not "shoveling," that's "stepping." That would be perfectly fine, wouldn't it? Of course it would. I wouldn't bend or stretch. I wouldn't exert at all. I would merely step. On a shovel. Which might cause it to push into the ground a little, only because of my normally-stepping weight, not because of any force applied by me. A totally passive action.

I looked right, then left. A gentle breeze stirred the juniper bushes. Somewhere in the distance, a dog barked. Out on the Strip, a tourist passed out from heat exhaustion. I narrowed my gaze at the grass bits.

The wisps of disrespectful grass were duly eliminated. I had absolutely not "done yard work" the day after surgery. I had merely stepped. Remember this line of reasoning when people try to scold you for doing too much during your recovery. It's like when you were a kid, and you (or one of the other kids) said, "If I happen to swing my fists around, like this: <windmill arm swings>, and you happen to accidentally walk into my fist, I am not punching you!" Same thing applies to shoveling. I mean, stepping. And as I stepped back into the house, I shook my grownup fist at the grass, threatening to return and do more shov...stepping, as needed.

Speaking of "gimme three steps," in these early days of recovery, I would do three trips up and down the stairs each day. This included two daytime naps. Every night I would carefully ascend the steps for the third time and get ready for bed. Sleeping wasn't too bad, although I could only lay on my left side, since the nighttime catheter bag had to hang off the left side of the bed. What the heck am I talking about? Well, somehow this notion got into my head and stayed there. It might have started in the hospital, where I was definitely constrained to left side orientation, what with all the tubing and various liquid management vessels. But back at home, every evening, I would remove the small, portable daytime catheter container, and attach the larger nighttime catheter apparatus to my left leg, always the left. And that somehow got me fixated on the notion that it always had to dangle off the left side of the bed at night, all night. A week into recovery, I realized I could have scooted over to the right side of the bed and moved the catheter tube to my right leg at any time, allowing the catheter to hang off over there, and I could have laid on my right side. I could have done this even in the middle of the night, just to allow for a change of sleeping direction. And yet, this seemingly obvious idea never occurred to me.

Sometimes I'm not too bright. Sometimes for seven days in a row. I could try to blame the hospital medication again, but I think that's a pretty weak defense. Anyway, I was very happy when I could finally lay on my right side, after seven days of being not too bright. Also, for the first time in more than a year, I didn't ever have to get up in the night to go pee.

Chapter 19 - Let's Get It Started

The nice medical people want to make sure that your entrails restart properly and begin processing food like they're supposed to. There are rare complications that can happen after surgery, and you don't want to be one of the rare cases. These rare complications can involve internal bleeding or some kind of blockage, which can mean something has gone drastically wrong. So, when it's been three days since you've come home from the hospital, and you've been eating more or less normally, yet you have not had a #2, you start worrying. You call the doctor's office. That phone call is the number one most popular post-surgery phone call they get at a urologist's office, according to my urologist's office. This is the call that asks, "I haven't had a #2 yet, am I going to die? Because the internet says I'm going to die."

Also, when you do finally have a #2, it's kind of black. So are the next couple ones. You jump on the Inter-Googles and discover that the black color means you're bleeding internally and you're going to die within the next hour. You now realize that your Las Vegas surgery team were all unqualified amateurs, they have not sewn you up correctly, and you're headed for the emergency room any minute now. This prompts the second most popular post-surgery phone call to the urologist's office. The call that asks, "Whose name do I put on the lawsuit, because the internet says I'm going to die..."

Relax. Yes, it's dark. Yes, that means there's some blood mixed in there. No, it's not cause for abject panic. You're not headed for the emergency room. Things will settle down and get back to normal, probably tomorrow. Be careful how you phrase these web searches when you go looking for answers. You can accidentally fill yourself with needless hysteria and a strong desire to initiate legal proceedings. Call your doctor's office. They'll talk you down off the ledge.

I was also looking forward to starting normal peeing operations one day soon. During my nine days of initial recovery, I would look at the catheter with disdain and mark the days on the calendar, counting down to when I would be free of that thing. Notice my choice of language. I can't even call it "my" catheter, it's "the." It's a very useful contraption, but it isn't much fun. And as much as I wanted it gone, I also dreaded its removal. I looked in horror at the installation and wondered what it would be like to get it pulled out of there. After all, I was completely and blissfully unconscious during its placement. I had made my humorous remarks to the surgery staff, and the next thing you know, boom, I wake up with that thing working away happily, as if magical fairies had come while I was knocked out, and gently caused it to be in there...probably with a generous sprinkling of magical fairy dust and a whimsical Irish chant. And that was definitely not going to be the case for the removal. When it came time for removal, I was going to be in that brightly lit room, where you are very awake and very alert, and if you're not careful, biopsies happen. Well, at least the reviled catheter was performing its function properly. Until one day.

Chapter 20 - When The Levee Breaks

There I was, in the living room. In my house, this is a room that contains many guitars, many amplifiers, a giant drum set, a somewhat less giant drum set, a stand full of keyboards, two framed Disneyland lithographs, a light-up Starbucks sign, all three *Powerpuff Girls* figures hanging from a lamp, a *Who Framed Roger Rabbit* beach towel, a talking Teletubbie ("La-La," if you must know), a highly collectible talking Pee Wee Herman figure, in original packaging, my dad's remains (in a box, on the mantle, displayed with a jar of Old Spice after-shave), and my computer/recording studio desk. Also, a mandolin and two banjos, which probably violates some city ordinance. I have applied for my open-carry banjo license. It's Vegas. They'll approve it.

There's also a lot of indistinct clutter everywhere. There's nowhere to sit, except for my computer chair and the seat behind the giant drum set. There are about 3 square inches of unused tabletop space, and the fireplace is mostly obscured by microphone cables. It's a great living room for entertaining guests, as long as the guests are there to play loud bashy music, and not lounge around chatting about the price of fish, or the state of roadwork in the neighborhood. It's just what a living room should be, I think.

Anyway, I was just standing by the keyboard rack one day, minding my own business, complying with the laws of the land, and not bothering anybody. And I felt a sensation that I had not felt in a very long time, a great disturbance in The Force, if you will. It was the urgent signal that it was time to go to the restroom and have an experience, pronto.

Well, that's okay, I thought. I have a catheter. No problem. Things will be handled in a medically efficient manner, with the appropriately installed equipment. I'll just continue standing here, admiring all my guitars. And then I peed all over the living room carpet. Not a little bit, either. Rather a lot. What in the actual hell?

As you can imagine, I was completely taken off guard by this turn of events. There's a hose shoved up in there. It's meant to convey the fluid directly to the collection vessel, without so much as a single errant drip. It had performed with excellent reliability for many days, and I had never once felt the sensation of "time to make your way to the bathroom." This deluge was accompanied by a very strong warning sensation, and it was not bluffing. I had no idea what was happening, but it didn't seem like it was according to plan. For all I knew, something had ruptured, or burst, or had become disconnected, or otherwise structurally failed up in there. You can imagine my confusion and dismay.

I took a moment to collect my thoughts and consider the situation. Nothing hurt, and everything felt okay. Over the next few hours, it didn't happen again, and everything went back to normal. I decided to just kept an eye on things, and I was heading to my 9-day follow-up in a couple of days anyway, so I resolved to bring it up at my appointment. Besides, there could be only one explanation: The Covert Urethra. A nefarious agent of chaos and destruction.

I need to jump ahead in the story for just a moment. After the catheter removal, I began to suspect that my doctor had secretly installed a second urethra, as a prank. I reasoned that it ran alongside, or possibly even inside of my normal urethra. It was probably equipped with a tiny isolinear computer chip (you know, the type they use in *Star Trek*), and placed by the robot arms. It operated with complete freedom and autonomy, but it was also programmed to wait until the comedy timing was just right, before dripping and dribbling at the most inopportune moment. Looking back, I now realize it was the only reasonable explanation. And on this day, while I calmly puttered around in my oddly furnished living room, inspecting the guitars and nodding approval at the drum set, Covert Urethra made his big flashy splashy debut. I resolved right then and there to have words with my prankster urologist about it. To this day, I'm still not convinced that Covert Urethra doesn't exist. I believe my urologist has dialed it back via remote control, to avoid further suspicion, but it's still in there. Your fun-loving doctor might try a similar stunt on you, just for a laugh. Remember, I warned you.

Chapter 21 - They Try To Make Me Go To Rehab

I didn't actually "go" to rehab, of course, but I was supposed to rehab myself at home, following expert guidance and instructions from doctors. "Don't lift anything over 7 pounds, for 30 days!" That's what the attending physician in the hospital had told me. The attending physician is a doctor who strolls around and dispenses advice and instructions to lots and lots of patients, who are not their actual patients. They're the substitute teacher equivalent of your hospital stay. Whatever they say is meant to hold you over until you can see your real doctor. I ran this 7-pound advice past my real doctor at my first follow-up visit, and asked him if that seemed right. He said no, don't lift over 15 pounds for another week or so. Your attending physician means well, but they're going to err on the side of caution, for obvious reasons.

Fortunately, a typical electric guitar only weighs about 8 or 9 pounds. But strapping one on and having it rest against my abdomen while in a standing position did not feel very nice. I performed all my guitar-based rehab in a sitting position, and I couldn't last more than a minute or two at a time, because sitting was also difficult. Operating a drum set was completely out of the question. I tried sitting on the drum seat, and even that was unpleasant.

I built myself a laptop riser out of various boxes, which allowed me to stand up while using the computer. I would get up in the morning and do standing activities for a couple of hours. Then I would go have a lie down, then do more standing activities. Then another lie down, more standing, then it was bedtime. You might not sit much for a few days - I sure didn't.

When it comes to resuming normal activity, I am not very patient. I looked wistfully at my motorcycle, knowing I absolutely could not ride it, all the while secretly planning to sneak a ride at my earliest opportunity. I did not repeat the shoveling (stepping!) activity, or attempt any other media stunts. Instead, I quietly moved around the house like a compliant patient, willing myself not to ever sneeze or cough. The thought of all that carefully crafted internal stitchery tearing loose with an uncontrollable ah-choo, terrified me. Somehow, I managed to stifle any violent abdominal respiratory spasms for several months. If you're in this situation, and you feel a sneeze or a cough coming on, let the fear well up and scare the daylights out of you. It works. You can also try staring at a bright light, or whatever other anti-sneeze method you like. But don't sneeze, unless you can figure out a way to do it while keeping your abdominal muscles completely relaxed (you can't). I used fear to scare the sneezes away.

Going up and down the stairs was getting easier all the time. So was getting in and out of bed. I had a pretty good handle on this recovery thing. After a few days back home, I successfully drove a car. That was a welcome accomplishment, since I could resume my Starbucks substance abuse problem. It was covid days, but according to local policy at the time, I was able to score my beverage and then immediately vacate the place. I could also get to the grocery store, where I would make my way very slowly up and down the aisles, remembering my three laps around the hospital floor. I gathered my grocery supplies like a 200-pound eggshell would do, scrupulously avoiding all the plague-infected shoppers.

I was still writing my own imaginary surgery results in my head, and I had made them look very rosy. I imagined myself miraculously cured, a marvel of medical science and an inspiration to all. But follow-up day was fast approaching, and I would have to hear the real version, and retire the fantasy story I had created. Nine days after surgery, I carefully placed myself in the car and headed off to my appointment.

Chapter 22 - Doctor Doctor, Gimme The News

"Well, it hadn't spread, but it was trying to. It was trying to leave the area. I think I got it all."

I focused on that last sentence. "I think I got it all." I was not pronounced cancer-free. Nobody is at this stage of the game. That comes later, after testing, if it comes at all. But on the bright side, at least it wasn't one of those follow-up visits where the doctor tells you that, once they got in there, they found half a dozen tumors the size of turnips, and an alien egg pod. He didn't confess to installing a Covert Urethra, but he wouldn't, would he? He probably had more laughs coming up, at my expense. After some further debriefing and reportage of the surgical proceedings, it was time for catheter removal.

Catheter removal. O joyous day. O happiness. O rapturous dawn of a new era. Let me tell ya, fellas, getting that thing out of you is a life-affirming event.

When the catheter is installed, water is used to inflate a bulb at the inner end of the tube, the end that's up inside your bladder. That's what keeps it in place. It can't fall out or work its way loose while you're sitting in Starbucks chatting with the gang, thank goodness.

Them: "Hey, what's that thing crawling across the floor?"

You: "Get back here! You're not finished working!"

Catheter: "Screw you, I'm getting a refill!"

So, when it gets removed, the first thing that happens is the little balloon on the inside is emptied of water, which means it can be pulled out without restriction. I know...it makes my insides feel squidgy just talking about it. And you're probably wondering the same thing I was, as I reclined on the exam table. I said the thing out loud, which was, "So, how bad an experience is this?" My doc replied with a very casual, "Eh, it's not bad," and 5 seconds later, splurch, out it came.

I must disclose that it did not actually make a "splurch" sound. I felt like I needed a sound effect to enhance the catheter removal story, and that's the one I'm going with. But in real life there's no sound effect. I was a little disappointed.

So anyway, what does it feel like? Much like you'd expect. It feels a bit like someone just pulled a thick rubber band out of there, a rubber band that's about two feet long. But it doesn't hurt, and it's over quickly. It just feels weird. Compared to your other experiences in that little exam room, this is a walk in the park. And the HPA is not present.

Speaking of catheters supposedly remaining solidly in place and never failing to route liquids into the designated collection vessel, I asked my doctor about the incident in the living room. The one where I was suddenly transformed into a large, non-housebroken puppy, randomly soaking the carpet. His answer was, "Oh yeah, that happens sometimes." He went on to say that, apparently, sometimes your bladder, which has endured a lot of abuse lately, decides to have a spasm. And when it does, it just routes its contents right around the catheter tube, where it was supposed to send them, and instead it all comes rushing out the usual passageway and onto the living room carpet, which was completely spotless before this incident (it definitely wasn't) and is now in need of extensive professional cleaning (it totally is). Once again, "Oh yeah, that happens sometimes."

After pulling the catheter loose and flinging it into the trash (good riddance!), your doctor will help you install an absorbent pad in your undies, as you are still trying to process what just happened, and voilà, you're done. You're free! O happy day! Savor this moment, boys. You will proudly strut to your car without indoor-outdoor plumbing accessories.

Chapter 23 - Poor Little Fool

Aw, look at him. Poor little fella. Is he okay? That's what I thought when I got home and looked at my formerly enormous penis.

Okay, let's just stop right here. Time out. When I say "formerly enormous," I mean six inches, and that's if I was flexing to get that last millimeter. Whatever! Believe me when I tell you I used to wield that thing in a very studly manner! Full of confidence and bravado!

Again, that might not be 100% true, but shut up. I'm "reimagining," like they do when they make a new version of some old classic movie that they should have left alone. Truth be told, I am a complete nerd-boy, always have been, and I learned how to play the guitar mostly so I wouldn't have to introduce myself to girls, and they would instead introduce themselves to me. When it comes to sexy time, terms like "studly," "confidence," and "bravado" probably do not belong in any description of me, much like the term "enormous."

In any case, what I saw after the catheter removal was the opposite of enormous, and more closely resembled my view of that thing from when I was in 6th grade. Not exactly majestic. Anyway, we've obviously come to the sexy part of the storybook, where we talk about penis size, which is probably what you were looking forward to the most. Hooray!

Sure, my formerly "enormous" penis had been through a terrible ordeal. No wonder it was shrunken in fear, and hiding as best it could. You would too, if you'd just had your manly innards sliced out and a rubbery tube thrust up in you, only to have that tube forcibly withdrawn nine days later. Who can blame the poor little fella? But there's more to the situation than simply hiding in fear.

What makes your boner the size that it is? It sure isn't the stretchy wrinkly skin on the outside. Nope, it's the urethra. Oh sure, there's erectile tissue and a few other odds and ends that contribute, but one thing is certain - your erection can't be longer than the stretch limit of your urethra. Your urethra is a tube that not only runs down the length of your weenie, it IS the length of your weenie. And now part of it is gone.

The prostate (if you have one) sits right on top of the urethra, and up against the bladder. When removing the prostate, it's just not practical to detach it from the urethra. So, a bit of the urethra gets cut loose and removed along with the prostate, then the doctor reattaches the remaining ends of the urethra to each other. What's the net result? Well, I lost about an inch. If you yourself are equipped with a "Big Ten Inch" (thank you, Aerosmith, for contributing such an obvious and gratuitous reference in support of the penis-y chapter), then easy math tells us that this loss will be less significant to you. But when you're merely "enormous" to begin with, it means a lot.

Now, you may get a lot of that back...eventually. But at least for now, you're going to be a little bit less "porn star" than you used to be. Not just in the size department either - also the firmness department. Especially in the firmness department. In fact, expect no firmness at all, at first, regardless of any quality stimulation. I mean, {*insert name of your favorite hot celebrity here*} could slink into your room tonight, lean seductively over you, her (or his) exquisite breasts (or not) brushing your face lightly, and say, "Is it okay if my girlfriend (or boyfriend) joins us?" And you would still produce the firmness of a melted gummy bear. For a number of obvious reasons, nobody is home down there at the scene of the crime and devastation. It's a war zone, and how can you expect firmness from a war zone?

Fortunately, there are pharmaceutical remedies.

Chapter 24 - The Harder They Come

(thanks to boner pills)

Oh listen, your doc will hook you up with a prescription for boner pills before your catheter is even cold, and still wriggling across the floor, trying to make a break for it. My doc wanted me <u>back up in the game, runnin' fast to take my swing</u>. (Apologies to Mark Morrison, who certainly never thought his hit song "Return Of The Mack" would be featured in a dribbly prostate story.) There will be a lot of "use it or lose it" talk, and most likely you'll be expected to take boner pills twice a week, for a couple of months. Do it. Swallow your pride (definitely not making a joke about that phrase here) and take the boner pills. The deal is, you need some good active blood flow happening down there if you're going to rehab that thing back to satisfactory operating condition. The pills do just that.

Erectile Dysfunction medications were an accidental discovery, as you may know. Pfizer was actually concocting a medication to dilate the heart's blood vessels as a way to treat cardiovascular problems. And then it was like, "Oh hey, look what else it does. Dang."

My prescription was for the brand of pills that are long-lasting. Not the famous ones with the name that sounds a bit like "Niagara Falls, except without the "Falls" part," the other ones. The ones that are meant to last a couple of days. And I was supposed to take one of those things twice a week, on Tuesdays and Fridays. Medically speaking, this is the best method for getting some enhanced blood flow going down there, in the interest of reanimating your apparatus.

You have to meet the boner pills halfway. It's not like you take the pill and suddenly, with no effort on your part, you're ready to stand in for Peter North in his latest adult video feature. The pills need some encouragement to get any result. This can be from your significant other, the aforementioned Peter North video, or any other stimulation that happens to be your particular preference, including your own self. Here's the thing for everyone to remember - keep your expectations low. In fact, maybe don't have any at all. This is going to take a minute, and training camp has just begun. You'll most likely get no results at all the first couple times you take the pill. Never mind. Enjoy the moderate headache and congestion, which are the most common side effects. The firmness will be along one day. Meanwhile, put some effort into the stimulation. And as you probably know, you can have a perfectly fine orgasm without having a lot of firmness.

For me, the boner pills produced some hint of firmness on the second try. Absolutely nothing the first time. Also, I soon realized that I got much better firmness results in the afternoon, and disappointing results at night. So, I changed my routine a little to accommodate my new strength and weakness. About three months in, I got what I would consider 100% firmness, pill-assisted. Your results may vary. Check with your doctor to see if boner pills are right for you. (They are.)

Every time I went to the pharmacy to refill my prescription, I felt the need to proclaim very adamantly that the boner pills were not for recreational use. "I'm a recovering cancer patient!" This is what I would yell at the nice pharmacist, who had already heard the same unsolicited line of defense from ten other old guys that day. "Are you familiar with this medication," they would ask. "Oh yes, but I don't want to take them, you understand...doctor's orders, formerly very studly, not a sad pervert at all, thank you…" They don't care. You don't owe them an explanation. I always gave them one anyway.

As I mentioned back in Chapter 1, I've always thought of myself as a bit of an overachiever in the firmness and enthusiasm categories, especially for my decrepit age group. So, I surprised my urologist with the report of my early progress. Six months in, I didn't need the boner pills to produce a completely firm result, although the thing was not yet operating at full pre-surgery level. It took a little while longer to get completely firm, and I didn't last very long before getting rubbery. But my favorite hobby, which had tried to kill me, was back.

I mean, now there is no fluid launching, of course. At this stage, you are now more of a pantomime artist, and your audience (if there is one) is just going to have to trust you when you claim you have "gotten your cookies." That's a little weird at first. As I've told a couple of friends, my orgasms have no punctuation now. You still get the big adrenaline rush, the same cardio surge, but no sudden "oomph" at the end. I wondered if I now had girl orgasms. I sometimes hear them described in this way. It's more like a wave, rather than a ramp up to a percussive finish. And without the percussive finish, you can play a little game, where you try to keep the adrenaline rush going for as long as you can. Like a surfer on a gnarly wave. This is probably how I'll eventually die - trying for a new record, until my cardiovascular system explodes.

I like the girl orgasms, don't get me wrong. It's just a little different now. And of course, there's no associated cleanup.

Chapter 25 - River Of Dreams

There is a seemingly endless arc of progress toward the goal of once again having dry undies after prostate surgery. This part of the experience is different from one guy to the next, with a lot of variation in the recovery timeline. One thing's for sure, after that catheter comes out, you're not going to be especially functional in the pee control department. All of your internal parts that are supposed to handle that process have been heavily damaged, and some of those parts are just gone for good. You'll recover, but it takes a long minute. Meanwhile, you're going to need a supply of pads. Not the thin ones. The big ones. And not the girl ones. The man ones.

Maybe you've seen the commercials. During the first few months of my recovery, I would get them in my YouTube viewing experience sometimes. YouTube, like all computer-based apps, knows exactly what you've been up to lately, and targets their advertising accordingly.

YouTube ad: "The only thing stronger than us...is you."

You: "Hey, don't patronize me! Look, this is just temporary! I'm not really a pad-wearing geriatric in real life! Look at me, I still look 40 years old! Okay, 50! Look, it doesn't matter...the point is, I am NOT that guy in the pad commercial, OKAY?"

I am that guy. We all are, all of us prostate-less geezers. Yes, it's temporary. (Most likely.) But you didn't choose the Pad Life, the Pad Life chose you. (Apologies to Tupac, who probably never thought his famous quote about "thug life" would one day be coopted and mangled by some drippy old fossil, wearing absorbent material in his drawers.) But there it is, we are pad guys, living the Pad Life, so get used to it.

There's a routine that you'll fall into. You wake up in the morning and slowly struggle to push yourself into a sitting position, trying not to use what's left of your abs. You look down and think to yourself, "Oh yeah...this thing." You stand, then you take off the briefs that you now always sleep in. Briefs. Not boxers. What's that you say? You hate briefs and have always been a boxers guy? Not anymore, son. Boxers don't work for pads, and you are now deeply into the Pad Life. You used to sleep naked, but that's not happening anytime soon either. Look on the bright side, the goddam catheter is gone.

You peel the overnight pad out of your undies, roll it up on its own adhesive strips, and park it somewhere. It does not get tossed into your bedroom wastebasket. That room smells enough like pee already, thank you very much. It's going straight to the kitchen trash can at your earliest opportunity. You now shuffle off to the shower, confident that you will have no drips on the way. However, after a couple of weeks, you notice many little dots on the bedroom carpet or floor. Huh. How did those get there?

You know how they got there, they came from you and that seeping little garden sprinkler of yours. Do what I did. Keep a washcloth at your bedside and clasp that thing over your leaky bits whenever you need to move around, padless. For now, that's basically to and from the shower. At all other times, you will be padded.

Once out of the shower and dried off, employ the absorbent bedside washcloth as needed, until you install a new pad in your fresh undies. When you're dressed, you go about your day. Don't forget to visit the restroom periodically. Sounds weird to have to say it, but you're going to notice that the usual alert signals from your brain are not nearly as strong as they used to be. They might even be completely gone, at first, like during catheter days. I found that I no longer got that sense of extreme urgency to go, no matter how urgent the situation really was. I still don't.

The conversation between you, your brain, and your bladder used to go something like this:

Brain: "Time to go."

Bladder: "Yeah, time to go."

You: "Yeah, hang on a minute, I just gotta finish this thing."

Brain: "No, right now!"

Bladder: "I mean, I could probably hold out for another 60 seconds..."

You: "I'm almost done doing the thing."

Brain: "Urgent! Urgent! Go now!"

Bladder: "Yeah, I'm losing my grip here..."
You: "Okay, just about done with the thing!"

Brain: "NOW NOW NOW!"

Bladder: "Gaah! Muscles...slipping...! Droplets...leaking...!"

You: "Okay, I'm running to the restroom now! Use emergency clamping force!"

Brain: "TOO LATE! RELEASE THE FLOODGATES!"

Bladder: "RELEASING...FLOODGATES...!"

You: "LET ME GET MY PANTS DOWN!"

Brain and Bladder: "YAAAAHH!"

You: "MY ZIPPER IS STUCK!"

Brain and Bladder: "YAAAAAAAAHHHH!!!"

You: "Whew. Made it."

Brain and Bladder: "Goddammit, dude."

It's a much more subdued message now, more like, "Hey if you feel like hitting the restroom sometime soon, you know, no rush, but if you feel like it..."

If it's been a couple of hours and you haven't gone, go anyway. When you do, you'll discover that you actually did have to go, by golly. Resist the urge, however, to go to the restroom every 15 minutes. The doctors tell us that we want a "quality" experience, not a big quantity of tiny pee breaks all day long. Quality, in this case, means there's actually enough of a reason to go in the first place, not three feeble drips. You'll get a feel for it, as you make your way through this exciting time of self-discovery.

Everything now feels just faintly different inside your lower abdomen, in a way that's hard to describe. No wonder...you're now missing part of the mechanism that used to manage this important bodily function. That also takes some getting used to. You keep waiting for the vague, familiar awareness of your missing innards to come back, and it never will. It's "A Whole New World" in there. (Thank you, Disney's *Aladdin*.) Remember that the prostate is jam-packed with nerve endings. Under normal conditions, it acts as sort of an all-purpose sensor array for the entire lower abdominal area. Once it's gone, you will be much less aware of all your lower gastro-intestinal functions.

Speaking of which, here's another thing I discovered - you also won't have the urgent brain signal that it's time to have a #2. And the need to have a #2 definitely affects the unintentional pee leakage. The extra pressure in there makes you much less capable of drip control. I know, we're spending a lot of time on dinner conversation here, and I'm sorry, but these are important matters. Look, at this moment, as I sit here writing this, I'm getting the faint brain message. In the old days, it would have been an urgent message. But I know, because of the time of day and because I recognize this faint signal now, that it's time for me to visit the gent's, and even though I am not getting the #2 message, I know that's going to be happening as well. Excuse me a moment...

...and I'm back. And I was right. I always am. Learn to notice the faint message, and your day will get less drippy. Use all the new skills you can get.

After a while, you start improving. You start your morning by resolving to not have any drips at all today. Two hours into your day you feel the first drips happen, and the pad does its thing. That's fine. You had a little seepage, but from this new moment, you're having no more drips today. Make that same resolution every day, as many times as the situation calls for it, and don't spend any time remembering how unsuccessful you were yesterday. Every new day is a clean slate. It's going to take approximately forever, but you will conquer.

One day, you'll choose to not change the pad you've had on all day, and just wear that same one all night, without installing a new one. The first time I tried this I had to immediately rethink my policy. Remember that pads are made so they absorb and disguise whatever minor wetness you might have produced, so while wearing a pad, you're never really sure about what's happened at night. But a week later it was fine. This is a big step. It's tangible evidence that things are slowly getting under control.

A day will come when you decide you're not going to wear a pad to bed anymore, because the pad seems dry when you wake up in the morning. Awesome. Give up the nighttime pad. Instead, stuff that bedside washcloth down there, just in case. Don't worry, it'll stay in the general area, even as you sleep. You'll be fine. In a laying down position, I found I was less likely to have drips anyway.

Now, during this time of transition, you might have to wash your sheets a little more often. That's also fine - you're on the road to recovery, racing forward at full speed. Take a leap of faith and ditch the nighttime pad. Change the sheets as needed and never look back! Freedom! Freedoooom! And when I say freedom, I mean sleeping naked for the first time since your catheter removal is going to feel amazing.

One day I decided I was going to go completely padless, all day. That lasted for approximately one day. But you don't know until you try. I tried it two more times before I swore them off altogether. You draw a line in the sand, and resolve to put up with any minor dampness that might happen. Once in a while, you'll notice that Covert Urethra has placed a penetrating wet dot, about the size of a quarter, visible to any casual observer, on the outside surface of your pants. This will happen when you're out in public, far from any restroom, because Covert Urethra is a master of comedy timing. That's why I favor untucked shirts as a style choice. You might also want to think about black pants.

So, the progression is:

1. Big thick pads, one for day, one for night.

2. Thinner, more comfy pads, one for day, one for night.

3. One thin pad for all day and all night.

4. One thin pad for day, no pad for night.

5. Freedom, liberty, and justice for all.

The pathway to dry undies is long, and it is also decidedly non-linear. I've lost count of the number of times I thought I was all recovered, only to have a particularly wet experience the very next day. It can be discouraging. Covert Urethra is weakening, but still able to harass you now and then. For me, after a few months, these false signals of success became a source of amusement. I would notice that I'd had two days in a row of total dryness and think, "There. That's all finished." And then I'd laugh at myself. Because no, it was not all finished, and I'd have three days in a row of reverse progress. I knew this would happen, each and every time I observed that I was "all finished." A couple of times I wondered if I should go back to wearing pads again. But I didn't, because I decided that would be admitting defeat, and whereas I am happy to admit setbacks and failures, I will not admit defeat. Neither should you.

I read some advice in another cancer memoir that recommended stuffing some toilet paper down there, if faced with an emergency. My advice: do not. Toilet paper is thin, flimsy, and clings to every surface, once it gets wet. You'll be picking toilet paper bits off of yourself for an hour. What you want is a paper towel. Something nice and durable, not soft and friendly. Maybe "the quicker picker-upper," for example. Paper towel material won't disintegrate and shred like toilet paper. Typical men's room paper towels are perfect. They're cheap, fairly durable, and not soft and comfy. Be generous. Fold it about four times. Maybe even use two. Trust me on this.

What exactly is the physiology behind this odd lack of bladder control? What's going in in there with all your plumbing? (Aside from Covert Urethra, of course.) Stand by for medical words.

Chapter 26 - Mama's Got A Squeeze Box

Look at you. You used to be full of sphincters. What happened to you, man? I'll tell you what happened. You were relieved of one of your sphincters and now you can't help peeing yourself.

A sphincter is a squeezy thing. That's what the doctors call it, I'm pretty sure. I guess a sphincter is actually a ring of muscle that surrounds and closes an opening or tube, such as the anus or the openings of the stomach. But for our purposes here, "squeezy thing" will do just fine.

I'll bet when doctors are hanging out at the country club, they can be heard to remark, "I removed a couple of squeezy things today. How about you, Jeff?"

"Oh, I haven't removed a squeezy thing since last Tuesday. More sparkling mineral water, Geoff?"

You have a lot of squeezy things - like, sixty of them, located all throughout your innards. But we're concerned here specifically with two, or possibly three of them.

Disclaimer - in my exhaustive research on this topic, I have found many sources that say we male dudes have two sphincters that control the pee situation - the internal and the external. And then there's this one particular source that says there are three. We're going with the two-sphincter model here, since that seems to be popular and correct.

And this I know for sure: womenfolk do not have as many sphincters as us dudes. To continue...

In your fully assembled, factory-fresh condition, you were issued two sphincters that contribute to the squeezing off of the pee source. First, there's the one in the bladder neck, which provides the major squeezing force. It operates without any say-so from you. It's totally automatic, a real self-starter, and does not need our permission to squeeze. And then there's the external sphincter (also called the striated sphincter), below the prostate. His name is "Lazy Squeezy."

That internal squeezy thing is fit and buff and ripped and hella squeezy. It has had a lifetime of squeezing, and is darn good at it. No wonder, because it gets yelled at by the brain over and over, about how it's time to go, RIGHT NOW! Lazy Squeezy, on the other hand, has never gone to the gym, does not own a Peloton, and has spent most of his life eating donuts, watching *Dancing With The Stars*, and letting the internal squeezy thing do all the heavy lifting. He helps out a little, but why put out a lot of effort when the gym-rat internal squeezy thing is so powerful and seems to enjoy his work so much? He's like a one-man version of Hans and Franz, from that *Saturday Night Live* skit, with the vaguely Austrian accents, that sound slightly like a former governor of California...those guys that are here to "Pump! <clap> You Up!"

That's what Lazy Squeezy thinks. And then he eats another maple bar.

Radical prostatectomy removes the internal squeezy thing, leaving only limp, slothful, donut-eating Lazy Squeezy to do all the work. Is it any wonder you can't get up out of a chair without baptizing yourself from the waist down? Hans and Franz, a.k.a. the internal squeezy thing, are no longer around.

As a result, when it comes to controlling your pee, you are now basically a girlyman. That's what Hans and Franz called you as the robot arms were tossing them into the wastebasket. You just didn't hear them, because you were unconscious.

Along with the absence of Hans and Franz comes an absence of the completely automatic interaction they used to have with your brain. Your brain can send the message, but there's nobody there to receive it except for Lazy Squeezy, who is still trying to get a handle on reliable brain communication. He is not able to interpret this message with the gravity it deserves. The sense of urgency to pee, followed immediately by the powerful automatic clampdown, is no longer possible, no matter how loud your brain yells.

Girls are not equipped with this musclebound assortment of sphincters when they are manufactured. They only get the one, and you might be wondering how women can possibly manage with only one pee-controlling sphincter. Well, theirs didn't spend a lifetime laying on the couch and eating donuts. It was working out every day, like Xena, Warrior Princess. And women use Squeezy Xena to her maximum potential, to at least clench for a couple of hours at a time, on the cross-country car ride. Remember when you used to moan about having to stop for a restroom break instead of driving straight through from Seattle to Lake Tahoe? Welcome to their world. And be glad that all women don't yell the Xena battle cry when it's restroom time.

The good news is, you can actually communicate directly with Lazy Squeezy. He was never automatic. He only responds to your direct commands. That means he can be trained.

Chapter 27 - Oh Kegel, Kegel, Kegel...

Oh Kegel, Kegel, Kegel...I squeeze you every day...

Oh Kegel, Kegel, Kegel...please squeeze the pee away.

That's a new holiday song I'm working on. Anyway, if you're a prostate cancer participant, you've probably heard an earful about Kegels by now. If not, well, on the sacred occasion of your catheter removal, you'll be given a comprehensive sheet that explains what Kegels are. For those of you not yet at this stage, I'll summarize.

Kegels are squeezy exercises. Specifically, they involve the squeezing of those pelvic floor muscles that help shut off the pee, shut off the poo, and clench like crazy when you've got the brakes locked up and you're skidding straight for that car that's stopped up ahead of you on the freeway. They are the muscles that squeeze on the first big drop when you've made the questionable choice to go on Disney's *Guardians Of The Galaxy* ride with the grandkids. This set of muscles is almost certainly in pretty good shape. But pretty good ain't gonna cut it.

In order to get Lazy Squeezy halfway functional, it's going to take peer pressure, and lots of it. Remember, after having lived approximately 60 years doing not much of anything, Lazy Squeezy doesn't even have a decent nerve connection to your brain. He prefers to be kind of hard to access, because that enhances his slacker lifestyle. So, the rest of the muscles in that area need to set an aggressive example. It's up to you to mobilize this platoon of pelvic floor muscles. Under your direction, they'll crowd around Lazy Squeezy, wearing their manly gym gear, and taunt him with remarks like, "Bro, do you even squeeze?"

You'll be instructed to do the Kegel squeezes for a certain number of reps and a certain number of sets, every day. My favorite part of the instruction sheet was where it said (I'm paraphrasing here), "Now that you've done your Kegels for three months, do them for the rest of your life."

The instruction sheet is not wrong in its intention. Don't worry, you can get a lot more casual about it after you've achieved reliable dryness. You might even be able to give them up entirely, one day. But for now, military discipline is called for.

Every morning you hop in the shower. While you're in there, it's time for morning Kegels. That's right, this is the best place to start. You're in there every morning, and it's part of your routine now. Do 'em! And let the drips fall where they may, because hey, you're in the shower! Private Kegel throws down every morning in the shower! Sir, yes sir! Another ten? Sir, yes sir!

Private Kegel finds opportunities to squeeze throughout the day. That's an advantage to this exercise program - it's totally invisible. You can do your reps and sets while you're in any location. Strolling through the mall, lounging at the beach, gambling away the mortgage payment in Vegas - anywhere! Squeeze out ten reps as you sit at a stop light. Another ten while you're in the chair at Supercuts. Nobody will know...unless you proudly announce it, of course.

"I'm doing my Kegels right now!" (Don't forget the euphoric grin.)

After doing Kegels properly for three months, your pelvic floor muscles, which were already in fairly good shape, are going to be extra powerful. You'll have GI Joe Kung Fu Grip down there. You'll be able to crush a charcoal briquette into a goddam diamond! Kegel Power! Once in a while, you will still have a dribble. But that will diminish with time.

On the day I got the catheter out, I had looked at the Kegel instruction sheet and scoffed. "Pff!" I said, as I sauntered casually to my car, "I'll have this thing licked in a couple of weeks." But of course, you're not supposed to start Kegels right away. You have to give your insides a chance to heal a little bit, so you have to wait a week. Still, a couple of months later, I had plenty of squeezing power. If I had the urge to go, I could clamp that thing down and wait it out, no problem. However, on many occasions, right after I had experienced a very satisfying restroom function, 30 seconds later there would be drips. This made no sense to me at all. Covert Urethra was not complying with company policy, and I was going to do something about it.

Turns out, "doing something about it" involves a lot of patience. As sure as I was that The Enemy Catheter had conspired with Covert Urethra to make my life difficult, possibly with cooperation and classified information from Lazy Squeezy, I had to finally admit that the blame might not lie completely with that gang, and there was no quick solution. Not even a medium-quick solution. You see, just because you can pulverize rocks with your pelvic floor muscles doesn't mean Lazy Squeezy has fully developed into the champion you need. That fully automatic squeeze function doesn't exist anymore, and you've got to train him to be proactive instead of reactive.

I had to mount a military campaign to starve Covert Urethra out of my system, and I vowed to do that with dogged focus and perseverance. Routine, routine, daily routine. Military discipline. To borrow a catch phrase from The Mandalorian, "This is the way." No need to overthink it, just shut up and carry out the routine, soldier. The payoff happens way down the trail. Six months out, I was happily going through my days with no pads, but with undies that were often just a little bit damp in the front. With each passing day, I noticed absolutely no improvement, but with each passing month, I noticed undeniable progress. To be fair, part of this is just healing time. Complete victory over Covert Urethra with 100% reliable dryness is a matter of letting your insides heal up, and also a military campaign of months...maybe a lot of months.

Some guys find that they never do get proper results, no matter how much dedication and effort they put out. For you guys, there's still help available. Special rehab methods can produce improvement, and there are always medical procedures that can mitigate your situation and give you control of things. You guys are in the small minority, but I haven't forgotten you. For a while it was looking like I might be one of you, and once in a great while, I still get a surprise drip. It took me well over a year to get dry, and there was a period where it looked like I had reached a state of no more progress. Eventually, I did cross the finish line, at a very slow pace. And once in a while I seem to take a little stroll back over to the wrong side of the finish line, maybe just to keep myself humble.

Talk to your doctor's office, they'll set you up with the right program. You might also ask about getting your Covert Urethra taken out. They'll pretend they don't know what you're talking about, but we know, don't we?

One last bit of strategy, regarding continence recovery: squeeze first, ask questions later. What I mean is, anytime you:

1. feel a sneeze coming

2. feel a cough coming

3. are about to lift something heavy

4. are about to run up some stairs

5. are about to drive over a speed bump

6. are heading for the final drop on Splash Mountain at Disneyland...

...squeeze first. It takes a while to get in the habit, but work on making it an automatic response that you don't even have to think about. Squeeze first. It's an easy victory, plus it's good extra conditioning. After all, Kegels shouldn't be a separate activity from daily life. Don't just do them as a morning and evening ritual. They should become a naturally occurring, spontaneous reaction to any upcoming bumps and bounces. Early in the game, you'll even want to pre-squeeze before you get up from a chair, before you climb into your car, and before you take your guitar down from its wall hanger. (If you don't have a guitar, get one, just to have. Having a guitar is cool.) After a while, even if you're surprised by a sudden jolt, your squeeze reflex will kick in, and even if you miss the first few drips, you'll still minimize the wetness. Here comes the speed bump...squeeze and hold it...over the speed bump...now relax. I can't emphasize this enough.

Full continence is not going to arrive with an announcement. It's going to sneak up on you, on little cat feet. You'll realize you've gotten there some time after you've gotten there. Sadly, a spotlight does not hit you, an awards show band does not play your walk-on music, and Vanna White does not do a graceful gesture to indicate your prize. That'd be cool, but it's not like that. It's anticlimactic, quiet, and hard to spot. Just like Covert Urethra.

Chapter 28 - Born To Be Wild or Dare To Be Stupid

I am one of those guys who is always looking for stunts to pull that are a little beyond my capabilities. This is sometimes because I want to overachieve and impress people and hit target goals before I'm expected to, and sometimes just to produce shock and surprise. This can lead to disappointment, but it can also lead to glory. Sometimes both. Here's an example from a long time ago.

Back when I was in touring rock and roll bar bands, it was a standard routine to go out for dinner after the show, usually around 2 or 3 in the morning. I had just finished a gig in Idaho Falls, at one of those big rock bars typically found in the western states. It was a lot like the place in Montana where I had been smashed over the head with my own guitar. Several of us from the band had gathered up a small assortment of groupies and headed out for some post-show dining at a fine 24-hour cafe. We had a lot of laughs and good-natured hijinks, and we had finished up the dining portion of the evening. One of the girls produced a cigarette and was preparing to light up, like smokers do after a meal. Now, I really dislike being around smokers at close range, and I saw an opportunity for a crowd-pleasing stunt. I abruptly lunged across the table, grabbed her cigarette just before the flame could touch it, and ate it. Just the cigarette, not the filter - I'm not an idiot. (I am totally an idiot.) But the rest of it, yes. Chewed it up and swallowed it all.

This produced exactly the reaction I was hoping for - surprise, horror, disbelief, and profound admiration. There was much uproar at our table, and the news travelled very quickly throughout the restaurant to customers and staff. I was an immediate legend.

I went back to the motel room, lost my dinner into the commode, decided it was totally worth it, and chalked up another victory in my own particular brand of sober-yet-daring rock and roll behavior. And I thought the incident was closed.

Two weeks and one emergency room visit later, I was flat on my back, spending several days recovering on a friend's couch. The chemicals in the tobacco had triggered a reaction in my blood stream, resulting in a spectacular multicolored rash from my ankles to my knees, painfully swollen joints, and the inability to move any faster than a 62-year-old cancer surgery patient. My evaluation after recovering from the blood poisoning: still totally worth it. This is who you're dealing with here.

So, about three weeks after my surgery, I was eyeballing my motorcycle. If I'm ever not riding it for a while, like when it's summertime and 150 degrees in Vegas, I always go out and start it up once a week and run it for a few minutes, just to keep the battery charged and the fuel system free of sludge. I could have started it up inside the garage. But it's loud and noisy in there, plus the exhaust fumes tend to accumulate, so of course I had to roll it out onto the driveway. I fired it up with a satisfying vroom-vroom and watched it idle for a minute. And I thought, you know, I'm feeling pretty good. I'll bet I could just take this thing around the block once and it'll be fine.

Once again, ladies and gentlemen, here he is! Eric, with the maturity of a 14-year-old! He's the kid who once ate a cigarette and gave himself blood poisoning!

I carefully positioned myself astride my motorbike and did a little test wiggle. Felt pretty okay. What the heck, I thought, I'll just do a brief little putt around the block. Just to splash the transmission fluid around. You can't do that by just letting it idle in the driveway, now can you? Besides, anytime I'm about to go over a bump of any kind, I'll simply rise up on the foot pegs and take the weight off my butt and abdomen, avoiding the bounce. Clearly, you can see the solid reasoning behind this plan. It was no more dangerous than shoveling - pardon me, STEPPING carefully and calmly, on a shovel, which was totally not yard work. Also, I would not be "riding," I would be "sitting."

It took me about 30 yards to realize that maybe this wasn't such a responsible choice after all. Oh, I employed the standing on foot pegs technique, but that little move takes more core strength than you think it's going to, especially when it comes to the core strength of a recent surgery patient. My innards did not protest super loudly, but they did say, "Ahem...pardon us, but what exactly do you think you're up to, mister?" However, I had committed, so I elected to complete my ride (sit) around the block...and when I say around the block, I might actually mean 3 blocks down, a couple of blocks over, across the train tracks, right turn onto Dean Martin Drive, a quarter mile alongside the 15 freeway, and then back down my street. I eased back into the driveway, eased the bike back into the garage, and eased myself back into the house. And I waited for signs of trouble. I was fine. No ill effects, no trip to the emergency room. Not a terribly grownup choice there, but I was fine. And upon reflection, I regret my little unauthorized joyride, mainly because if I had messed something up in there, I would have been disrespecting the work that skilled medical professionals had done in order to save my life. It was a selfish choice, much more so than the cigarette stunt, because there were doctors whose time I might have wasted. I've never confessed this to anyone who matters, but don't worry, none of them are going to read this book.

My motorcycle, upon which I sat.

Chapter 29 - Further On Up The Road

I spent the first three months after surgery trying not to do anything too stupid, with reasonable, if not complete success. By a convenient coincidence, I had gotten prostate surgery in the middle of a pandemic, and I was comprehensively unemployed. That made recovery pretty easy, as I had no reason to lift speaker boxes, run cables, or push audio equipment through Vegas casino hallways. I settled back into my covid era routine of daily Starbucks, twice-weekly Guitar Center visits, and playing guitar for nobody, in my living room. I bought guitars and amps off the internet to relieve the boredom, and I sold guitars and amps on the internet after growing tired of them. I also confirmed that I hate retirement, and reaffirmed my personal vow to never retire for real.

At the three-month mark, it was time for another PSA blood test. The moment of truth. Was I cured? Was I still diseased? It's not like the circumstances were ideal. I had gotten a qualified "I think I got it all" from my doctor, but my particular flavor of cancer was pretty aggressive, and once again it seemed like I could not exactly count on good news as a sure thing.

To my complete surprise, my PSA level came back undetectable, less than the lowest possible amount they can measure. Utterly amazing. I was cancer-free! How did that happen? I decided all the credit should go to my urologist/surgeon, who had clearly paid attention during the prostate operation lecture in med school, and was definitely not cutting class to spend the day at the beach. Undetectable. Can you beat that?

I got java chips in my Frappuccino, to celebrate. And I might have also bought another guitar. An expensive one.

Another interesting side note here, calling way back to my day of surgery, when I had observed the destruction of my belly ring (bar) location. As things healed over the next couple of months, it began to look like there might be part of the hole still intact, and it looked like the incision might have just missed the piercing site. I had wondered if maybe one day I might get it re-pierced. So, long about this time, three months on from surgery day, I tentatively tried to stick my jewelry in there, just to see how far it would go. And with some effort, and some ointment making things as slippery as possible, it went about halfway in.

About a week later, I went to a tattoo and piercing shop, to see about maybe getting that thing reinstalled. I had a fairly terrifying conversation with the piercing guy, a conversation which included him using the phrase "bulldogging it in there." Mind you, this was a guy who had several face piercings, one of which looked infected.

I passed on his plan, which seemed to include more violence than I was prepared for. Instead, I went home and examined my piece of age-inappropriate belly jewelry, and noticed that it had external threads, and I was sure that was part of the difficulty. Some of these items have threads inside the end of the bar for screwing the ball end in place, and some, like this one, have external threads. The external threads were grabbing too much on the delicate skin, and not sliding smoothly. So I tried an experiment. I took a dental pick, which has a smooth, curved metal end, and also has a smaller thickness than the belly bar, and I poked it into the hole with some antibiotic ointment. I did this for about two weeks, carefully wiggling it and encouraging it to reach a little further each time. And one day, it went all the way through. The next day I had my belly bar back in, with no "bulldogging" involved.

Once again, in case you think I'm not being serious: maturity of a 14-year-old.

Chapter 30 - Guess Who's Back...Back Again...

Another 3 months had gone by, and I recovered and rehabilitated a bit more. I glided into my 6-month PSA test with a casual air of contentment. At the 3-month mark, I had been undetectable and cancer-free. Now I was feeling good, my underwear was only slightly damp, and my numb spot was even showing signs of improvement. I could lift things, I could run short distances, and I could easily get my "massive" 5 inches 100% firm with no boner pills (oh look, it's adorable!), as long as I preceded the event with 48 hours of nothing but pure thoughts. (That method doesn't work very well on PSA levels, but it did help encourage the firmness.) The world was my oyster and I was once again fully prepared to live to 100. Imagine my consternation when that PSA test came back at 0.2.

After prostate removal, I'm told that it's not unusual to have a PSA of about 0.2, due to a few stray antigens still floating around. Then it's supposed to fall to undetectable in the months that follow, as the stray antigens die off and no new ones are created. That's what's supposed to happen, and I had beaten that goal by registering an undetectable PSA level at three months. Mind you, 0.2 is nearly the lowest measurable amount, so we're not talking about a four-alarm fire here. But my recovery had gone backwards in this department. I started off with the undetectable reading at 3 months, then progressed (regressed?) upward to 0.2. I had transitioned from cancer survivor back to cancer patient. What happened?

This is called a biochemical recurrence. With the removal of the useless lump of prostate, nearly all cancer cells had been successfully evicted, but let's face it, a cell is a tiny little thing. It's impossible to get every last one, even with robot arms. What happens sometimes is that there are a few cancer-y cells left by the wayside, and they start recovering. There's no prostate anymore, but there are enough stray prostate cells still hanging around where it used to live, and the ghost of Clint Eastwood rises up from the grave and yells, "Get off my lawn!" again, only this time with a more ghostly voice. There's an airy, wobbly reverberation to his voice, like in a *Scooby-Doo* episode. Then Ghost Clint throws half a handful of antibodies around, in a feeble gesture of dissuasion. He's a weak and pathetic wisp of his former self. But he's just warming up. A biochemical recurrence can rev up into full blown prostate cancer, even without an actual prostate to fuel it. It can also travel to other parts of you and set up camp, just like all the other cancer types.

I had enjoyed being cured of cancer for three months, and now it had come back to haunt me. This happens sometimes, and it calls for you to enact a new strategy. The important thing to discover at this point is how long it takes for the PSA level to double. That gives you an idea of how fast old Ghost Clint is growing in there, and how proactive you want to be in combating another bout of prostate cancer, in a body that has no prostate.

Funny thing about that - I was told by one of my doctors about a guy who had a PSA level of over 1,300. That's right, one thousand three hundred. And this guy had no prostate. How is that even possible? See, that level is way more than a prostate can produce, if you have one. The answer is, his prostate cancer had metastasized into his bones, turning his entire skeleton into a giant PSA production factory. In contrast, my 0.2 seemed pretty insignificant. Still, I really didn't want to turn into that guy. So we formed a plan.

I was instructed to get yet another PSA blood draw, in six weeks this time, not three months. You want eyes on that number pretty often, just in case things are about to get out of hand and rise to 1,300. Once again, I would be waiting for the results of an important test. I was getting good at it. I thought briefly, once again, about a European vacation.

Six weeks later I got another blood draw, and my PSA level was 0.2 again. Huh. What now? On one hand, I was pretty cheered up that it hadn't risen back to 33. (Okay, 29! Jeez! Let it go!) On the other hand, I admit I was a little disappointed that my PSA level was being so agnostic. I thought, come on, either disappear completely, or jump up to some halfway meaningful number! Give me a reason to take a course of action! Don't just sit there like a lazy sphincter, eating donuts! By the way, in case you're wondering, yes, I did jump on the Inter-Googles and try to look up if orgasms can affect a PSA level after one no longer has a prostate. I couldn't find a single mention of it, so I'm assuming no. I was told...you guessed it...go get another PSA blood draw in another three months.

By this time, I had reconsidered my criticism of my PSA level's lack of commitment to drama. I had decided that sitting at 0.2 forever would be just fine, after all. Alas, that was not to be. My next result came back at 0.4. It seemed I was officially cancer-y again.

Well, that took the wind out of my sails for a minute. The big surgery, the recovery, all for nothing. I remembered back to the 12 positive biopsy samples, the high Jackie Gleason number, and the "it was trying to leave the area" remark, and I was not completely surprised. Still, having a PSA of "undetectable" after the surgery had instilled within me a certain cautious optimism (okay, reckless optimism), and that was now gone.

It was decided, by my doctor and me, that I would get a blast of radiation in the near future, and with any luck, that would snuff out Ghost Clint for good. But that's a story for another time.

Chapter 31 - Just A Song Before I Go

This is supposed to be where the guy telling the story admonishes all the other old dudes to go get checked out. I am not here to do that. Get checked out if you want to, or if it's more your style, be like Warren Zevon. I'm not here to judge or push you in any particular direction. I'm telling you my little story, and it's mostly for entertainment purposes, not so much for handing out loads of unsolicited advice. I myself, in contrast to my old ways, have assembled a small collection of doctors whom I allow to examine and rebuild me as needed. For how long? Well, that's yet to be determined. But at least for right now, and right now is all that's important.

If you want to live to be old, I guess go see doctors, and that'll increase the likelihood of you becoming an old guy. If you want to be reckless and take chances and scoff at advice, that's okay too. There's more to life than being careful. Eating a cigarette, for example, makes a great story. So does skydiving, which I have done, so does playing rock and roll songs in an arena in front of 17,000 people, which I have done, and so does going 135 mph down a Nevada highway on a motorcycle, which I have done more than once. I have been naked onstage in front of an audience numerous times, I've watched a big chunk of a glacier fall into the ocean, in Alaska, and I narrowly missed catching a stray bullet when a gunfight broke out in a bar, where I was playing drums. These and many other experiences add up to a decently exciting life. And after all, there's a popular saying that claims, "Great memories begin with bad choices." We hear that a lot in Vegas. Our whole economy is based on it.

Then again, if you do take steps to be a little bit careful, there's probably going to be more time and opportunity for you to decorate the world with your weirdo personality, and that's what I finally decided to do. Choose your own path. Your results may vary.

Closing Number - Carry On, Wayward Son

Carry on, champion. Whether you've just started waking up in the night to go pee, or if you've just typed "urologist" into a search engine for the first time.

If you're waiting for the results of your first PSA test.

If you're about to get "the finger" for the first time.

If you're staggering, light-headed, away from your prostate biopsy.

If you're looking at a Gleason score that makes you furrow your brow.

If you've just given up trying to look cool in front of the hot physician's assistant.

If you've just left a radiology lab covered in fluid that was supposed to go into your vein.

When you're staring down the long empty corridor of incontinence recovery.

When you're staring down the long empty corridor of "it's too far advanced, there's nothing we can do."

Carry on, champion. Ride fast, smash life over the head with its own guitar. Decorate the world with your weirdo personality, in whatever time you have left. Live to be 100, even if you only live to be 50. I'm counting on you.

Photo Credit: Meneldor Photography

⸱ENCORE⸱

*Yes, I know, musical theater productions don't have encores.
They don't have closing credits either, but that's coming up as
well. Shush. I'm "deconstructing the genre," or "reimagining
the paradigm," or something. You probably noticed that I ended
Chapter 31 rather abruptly, and probably knew that it was a
fake ending. And I know that a lot of guys might want to know
what the radiation experience is like. Therefore…*

"What's that? You wanna hear another one?"

<crowd screaming>

"I can't hear youuuu…!"

Crowd: "Just get on with it! The babysitter is on overtime!"

Encore, Part I - Fade Away And Radiate

It had been a year since I had Clint Eastwood removed, and what with Ghost Clint and his PSA-inducing stray cells causing havoc in the neighborhood, I was starting a course of radiation. And that meant getting an Axumin scan. This is a type of PET scan, designed to precisely locate and identify juvenile delinquent prostate cancer traces after you no longer have a prostate, and lecture them sternly about their lack of proper deportment and woefully inadequate contribution to society. This lecture concludes with, "And I've got my eye on you!" Picture the old Dragnet TV episode where Sargent Friday delivers the marijuana lecture to the snotty teens. That's how this scan works.

Axumin is the stuff they inject into you. It's basically radioactive sugar, and apparently, when you're having a biochemical recurrence, it's very good at shining a spotlight on juvenile delinquent prostate cancer remnants...the ones that think they can just terrorize a neighborhood that doesn't even have a prostate anymore. Although they are juvenile delinquents, Ghost Clint is actually kind of in favor of these young ruffians, and secretly does not mind them on his lawn, because they remember him and tell stories about him and generally keep his memory going.

A good jolt of non-lethal radiation was on my horizon. I was looking forward to glowing in the dark and acquiring unexpected new super powers. If I know anything about radiation, I know it gives you super powers. I reckon the Axumin primes your system, then the radiation blast activates the super powers, probably because a careless lab technician accidentally bumped the control up to "lethal." I was hoping my new super power would be enhanced guitar playing. My new stage name would be Radioactive Sugar. My first album would be called Axumin: Bold As Love. (Apologies to Jimi Hendrix, whose album *Axis: Bold As Love* stands as a timeless monument to Rock and Roll guitar artistry.) (Further apologies to Sugar, the singer for The Ohio Players. He is not radioactive.)

I decided to try a different radiology place this time...one that did not have Elite CT Scan Team #1. One exciting visit with that bunch was enough. So I made an appointment at a new lab, one that specializes in this exact scan procedure.

Before your Axumin scan, which is going to detect any new little lumps of recurring prostate cancer, you're required to eat high protein for 24 hours, no sugar at all, and no carbs at all. You can't exercise (oh dang, I was totally going to do 5 miles on the treadmill, with my personal trainer, Lazy Squeezy). And they don't even want you lifting anything heavy. Then, for 4 hours before you come in, it's no eating or drinking, not even water. This is all because cancer feeds on sugar, and they want to starve your leftover cancer, to get it really desperate and excited about what's going to happen. When they inject the radioactive sugar, your recurring cancer is all like, "Finally! Jeez, I'm starving here! Gimme!" All the cancer cells start gobbling up the radioactive sugar like it's their last meal, and the radioactivity then helps produce an image of where all the Axumin has landed, and presto, there's a target to shoot at. Sargent Friday has his eye on you.

Once at the scan lab, you remove any metal items, get stuck in with the IV line, and have a lie down on the slab. As long as you're there, inside a fancy scanner tube, they go ahead and do a CT scan first. I mean, why not? You bought the vacation package, might as well take advantage of the free CT scan. It'll make a nice souvenir. Then your technician will shoot the radioactive stuff in, and you proceed to remain completely still for about 25 minutes. You do get to breathe. But apart from that, you pretend like you're getting your picture taken in the late 1800s. You want the image nice and clear.

My lab guy was incredibly pro. A very serious and detail-oriented dude, he was also very pleasant. And he was military-style organized. Really informative, really focused. Turns out he was the head supervisor for all the radiology lab technicians in the Las Vegas valley, so no wonder he was so focused and organized. And he offered me a nice pillow for behind-the-knees support, which I took. 25 minutes later, I was up and out of there.

The Axumin scan is the most precise, detailed, and accurate scan of its kind. It can spot a tiny mass. But it can't spot an individual cell. So, when I got the result of my scan, it showed absolutely nothing. My doctor said, "Well, whatever cancer you have in there is microscopic." That's great news, all except for those three words from the middle of the sentence, "cancer you have." Out of context, it sounds like Yoda is giving me my prognosis:

"Cancer, you have. Treatment, you will get. Mmmm!"

<levitates X-wing fighter>

My doctor had said that, with radiation, he was confident I could still be cured. That all sounded good, but I had questions. Like, if there's no visible image from the Axumin scan, how will anybody know what to shoot at? Also, since my PSA was a tiny little 0.4, should I put off radiation for a while?

I was given basic answers to these questions, but I was also given a consultation appointment with a radiation place, which was in the same building as my doctor's office. There, I was assured, I would get detailed answers. And boy howdy, did I ever.

My new radiation oncologist talked with me for an hour and a half, in person. How often, in this day and age, do you get that much time with a doctor? (I mean, while you're not under general anesthesia, of course.) He explained all about the modern data management and fancy algorithms that they use. The targeting of your treatment is based on extensive studies of biopsy patterns, and computerized number crunching of a couple of million cases' worth of data from prostate cancer biochemical recurrences. There's a mind-boggling database of where the recurring cancer goes, and then that all gets tailored to your particular situation. Even in the absence of a visible scan, they still know where it's going to be. Ghost Clint, it turns out, has predictable patterns of behavior.

Your first visit to your radiation oncologist is a detailed professional consultation. But your second visit involves tattoos! And they're done by hand, prison style, with just a bare needle and India ink! How rad is that? Sadly, although I had requested a dragon on one side and a flaming skull on the other, you just get three dots. Three little black dots, one on your left hip, one on your right, and one right above your massive five inches, near your pubic bone. These three dots will be used by the targeting scanner, to locate and remember your exact position, for the next 40 visits. At each visit, they orient you on the slab in such a way that green lasers align with your spiffy new tattoos. As my last dot was being made, I asked the technician how it was going. She replied, "I'm just finishing the skull!" And I knew I was going to like it in that lab.

I began my 8 weeks of fancy radiation, 5 days a week - 40 treatments total - from the fancy 2.2 million dollar linear accelerator. (My radiation oncologist seemed to really enjoy quoting this figure.) This beastly contraption circles its way around you, as you lie on the slab. Every day before you head to your treatment, you have to go to the bathroom and have a #2, then drink 32 ounces of water as fast as possible, about half an hour before your appointment. They want your bowels empty and your bladder full, because this helps push things around in there, in a way that will minimize the collateral radiation damage to your nearby internal parts.

Each day you check in at the front desk, get your temperature taken with one of those forehead laser gizmos (well, I did...this was during the time of the covid delta variant), and wait to be summoned to what I always called "the transporter room." At my radiation place there was a light-up sign outside the door that said, "Beam On," hence the *Star Trek* reference.

Once called from the waiting room, you go back to the transporter room, recite your birth date as confirmation of identity, agree that it is your picture on the computer monitor, and take off your shoes. If you're me, you have also removed your age-inappropriate belly ring, so it doesn't accidentally get turned into plutonium, or something. Then you hop on the slab of the fancy machine, get your prison tattoos aligned with the green lasers, and hold still. Ten minutes later, you're out. Repeat 39 more times.

On the subject of holding still, you want to hold still, for reals. You don't want to be the guy who was ahead of me one day, who did not hold still. Here's what I heard from my waiting spot in the hallway, as another dude was getting the treatment:

Radiation technician, over the intercom: "What are you doing?!"

Radiation technician to other radiation technician: "Why is his arm up?!"

Radiation technician, over the intercom: "Please put your arm down!"

Radiation technician to other radiation technician: "Well, the damage is done."

Apparently, this patient decided it would be a fun idea to reach up and touch the emitter as it passed overhead, which did not exactly help the accuracy of the beam. Upon leaving the transporter room, he explained to the incredulous technician that his arm fell asleep and he was trying to get the circulation going again. This involved a certain amount of getting completely misaligned with the green lasers. So the beam was shooting at who-knows-what as it passed overhead, and then touching the contraption misaligned it even more. Here's my advice - don't do that. Suffer for a minute with your tingly arm, and when the beam is finished, you can shake it off. The thing is shooting high powered radiation, for Pete's sake.

If you're going to be getting this treatment, you can look forward to possible chronic fatigue, some bowel weirdness, maybe a temporary step backwards in the incontinence department, and maybe some burning sensations while going wee. They give you a list of all the delicious, exciting foods to avoid if you're having burning sensations. You can't have superb back-of-medical-lab tacos, for example. I did not alter my diet at all, and I had no burning. I wish the same good luck for you, if you're getting ready for this treatment. Don't give up tacos unless you really have to.

Speaking of burning, you do not get burnt skin. Unlike some other types of cancer radiation, this one does not cause skin damage. That's a plus. I have known radiation patients that have gotten pretty toasted, and they had to use the special high-grade medical lotion, available at the hospital pharmacy.

For most of you radioactive guys, you will experience the onset of side effects starting at about halfway through the course of treatment. And they typically disappear within a few weeks of finishing. A handful of guys report no side effects at all during the whole course, and a very small handful of guys are really miserable, starting at the end of the first week and continuing all the way through. My side effects, which were pretty mild, happened around at the end of the first week, then mostly disappeared a week later. During my course of treatment, I got a little tired overall, with two days of extra-severe tiredness in week 1. I had a couple of hot flashes (Where my menopausal ladies at?! Woo-hoo!), and things got a little soft in the bathroom department for a week or so. Then everything pretty well settled back to normal.

After I was all done with the 40 treatments, it took about a week before I noticed that a certain sensation was starting to disappear. It's hard to explain, but there was a feeling that had slowly built up in the place where my prostate used to be, a "fragile" feeling, similar to the later stages of surgery recovery. A faint version of that. And then, after the radiation course had been completed, it became much less noticeable, gradually diminishing over the next few weeks. I reckon that was radiation damage healing itself. It wasn't until months later that I realized that healing was still happening...it takes longer than you think it will.

Also, hilariously, after downing the large daily quantity of water and keeping it in there until my sessions were done, I started experiencing the same thing that got me started on this whole adventure. After escaping the linear accelerator beast, I would go wee, nothing more would come out, and it felt like I wasn't finished. 15 minutes later, when I got home, I had to go again. And then half an hour after that, one more time. All this fuss, just to return to my original warning symptoms from two years previous. Could have saved myself the trouble.

Not only did all my side effect symptoms mostly solve themselves, I actually kept feeling slightly better as the weeks of treatment went on. At my weekly chat with my doctor, I would reluctantly report that I had nothing alarming to reveal. They like that. "We like boring," they would all say.

Mind you, in addition to the "not finished" feeling, which lingered for a while, I also had a slight return to the occasional unauthorized drip, and this happened near the end of the course of treatment. It took a couple of months to sort out, and I resumed more aggressive Kegels, just to encourage radiation-damaged Lazy Squeezy to get back in shape. He was using the radiation as a tanning bed and sipping Frappuccinos, as it turns out. And I further realized that the radiation had temporarily re-animated Covert Urethra, master of comedy timing. Every time I think I have that thing beaten into submission, it makes another appearance, just to prevent me from wearing khaki cargo shorts in public. And I have to wrestle it to the ground, punch it in the junk, and reestablish who's boss. But I've found that it only takes a couple of days of serious Kegel power to regain reliable dryness. Lazy Squeezy is not a bad guy, and he really is on your side. He's just...well, lazy.

Oh hey, here's another thing you might look forward to if you get blasted with radiation - "brain fog." A lot of people have heard of "chemo brain," which is the general confusion and inability to focus after having had chemotherapy. But radiation can cause it as well. Heck, even the cancer itself can cause it. Take it from me, it's not super fun. And it'll sneak up on you. You'll be setting up a sound system for a corporate event, and suddenly find yourself standing in the middle of the ballroom, staring blankly at the garish casino carpet, as you try to remember how to connect all the audio cabling that you've connected a zillion times before.

It can get especially bad if you're trying to multitask. So, don't. Do the one thing, then go do the next thing. Do not prepare and send invoices to clients while you're eating lunch, watching YouTube videos, and taking a phone call. One or all of those things will turn out disastrous.

I won't go into a lot of detail on this topic here - that's what the internet is for. But I myself had to have a chat with a couple of important people in my life, along the lines of, "Hey, keep an eye on me. I feel like I might be having early onset dementia, or something."

It'll probably get better, somewhere between right after you finish with your radiation treatment, and never. Hard to say. And it varies a lot from one guy to the next. You can take steps to refocus yourself. Start making lists, and use that calendar in your phone. Even for the easy stuff. Just filling out the calendar will help you get a handle on the fog. Narrate your tasks as you do them. Basically, be your own commentator, as if you're doing a voice-over for an autobiographical documentary. Maybe not in your loud outside voice, but at least murmur to yourself. I got in the habit of narrating my gathering and packing of musical gear when preparing for musician gigs, multiple times for each occasion. Otherwise, I might easily leave the house without a guitar. (Disclaimer: I have done that more than once, and that was years ago. So, some of this ditziness is built-in, in my case.)

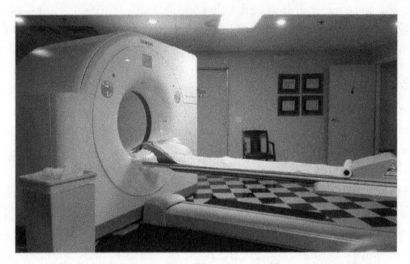

The Axumin scanner. The CT scanner and bone scanner are
similar to this thing. But I wasn't taking pictures at that point.

Beam on! The door to the transporter room. Note the thickness of that door (and surrounding walls, of course).

Encore, Part II - Energized

The front office staff and the technicians were all awesome at the radiation place, and it was like comedy-spa-day, with me providing a lot of the comedy. There was some unavoidable social interaction with the other cancer dudes sometimes, because the patients are coming and going at a fast pace. As I mentioned, the actual treatments only take about ten minutes, and eight minutes of that is fiddling with your shoes, getting situated in the machine, and getting your drawers pulled up afterwards. So a lot of guys are going through the place every day. I'm not big on social interaction with strangers, particularly in men's rooms ("Now I pee like a two-year-old!") or in doctor's offices, especially with guys my own age. A lot of this is because they, unlike me, do not have the maturity level of a 14-year-old. They seem like grownups, which makes me uneasy. But I tried to blend in as best I could.

On my first treatment day, another patient, sporting a Portland Drum Shop t-shirt, came out of the transporter room, and I said, "Hello, mister drummer." He looked at my NASA t-shirt and replied, "Hello, mister astronaut. Did ya get that at Houston?" Me: "Kennedy." A nice, short interaction, just the way I like it.

On another day, as I was coming out of the transporter room, I said to the next guy, "How ya doin', champion?" He replied with, "Are you the one hogging all the radiation?" We had a laugh, and I assured him that I was definitely hogging all the radiation, but they were filling the machine back up for him. And in he went. See, this is totally fine.

But I had heard another guy in the waiting room one day, bending some other poor guy's ear about every single football game, college and pro, that had ever happened in America. He was quoting dozens of stats from the past 50 years. And he was offering expert opinion and psychological analysis about every running back in the history of the game. He did all this with an air of complete confidence, relentless detail, and a level of pontification that implies, "Don't argue with me, I know all the things," and I really, really didn't want to chat with that guy. So I mostly kept my head down, tried to look vaguely like a weirdo (that was the easy part), and quickly scurried to the transporter room when they called me. Once out of the waiting room and back in the transporter room, the dynamic would change a bit. Because there were fellow weirdos working back there.

One day, upon entering the transporter room, I observed that my official picture, which came up every day on the monitor, along with all my important data, was a soot sprite. That's a character from the great animated movie *Spirited Away*, by Hayao Miyazaki. I had worn a *Spirited Away* t-shirt a couple of days before, and one of the technicians, who is a huge Miyazaki fan, violated policy and replaced my official picture with one of those cute little spiky black fuzzballs. It was supposed to be temporary, but my soot sprite picture remained in place for the duration of my treatments.

That technician was also a huge *Star Trek* fan, so one day I asked if there was any chance he could say, "Energize" on the intercom, just when the beam was turned on. As you may recall, there's an intercom and camera system between the transporter room and the control room, in case they have to issue frantic instructions to a patient who has just raised his arm to touch the beast in mid-radiation blast. The reply to my request: "Well, I'm pretty sure I'm not allowed to do that. Then again, I'm pretty sure rules were made to be broken."

I took my position on the slab. Everybody cleared the room, and the beast did its x-ray routine. They use an x-ray before your actual blast of radiation, to have a good look at your entrails and evaluate their position, make sure you're containing a reasonably uncomfortable amount of water, and have a quick look at the status of last night's dinner. If everything passes inspection, you're good to go. The slab did its usual fine-tune position shifting. It does this to scoot you into the perfect position, guided by the lasers. The beast rotated and set itself up for the radiation pass.

Right before the beam went on... "Energize!"

It made me so happy. I had to fight to hold still and not laugh. The machine did its first pass. In my radiation regimen, I got two passes. The beam went off, and the beast set itself up to do the return pass. And, through the speakers I hear...

"Captain, I'm givin' her all she's got!"

Beam On. Second pass.

I nearly wet myself. But I gritted my teeth and held still. It was all I could do to keep it together. It was the highlight of my radiation course.

The very next day, I was lying on the slab as the machine was setting itself up for the x-ray imaging, and the theme song from the original *Star Trek* series suddenly came on the overhead speakers. Not the short version from the TV show, the long, extended, full length version. It was followed by the *Star Trek Next Generation* theme, again, the full-length version. And right before the second pass... "Energize!" from another one of the technicians. As I was getting up off the slab, I professed my undying love to the crew.

That's the kind of vibe I had with the radiation gang. Cartoons and *Star Trek*. And policy violations. And just for the record, none of those shenanigans ever actually happened. I'm making it all up. It's a complete fiction. So, nobody's in trouble. Okay? Okay.

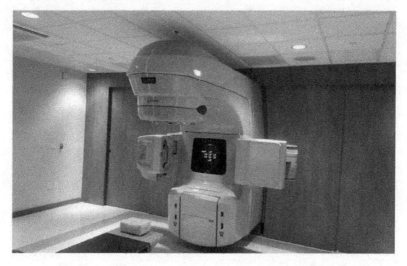

The Beast. That entire structure comes out from the wall
and rotates around you, in the vertical plane. Do not touch it.

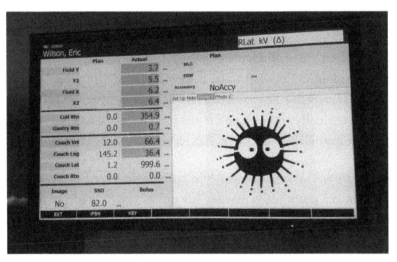

My data page at the radiation place.
This picture, which is supposed to be me, but which is in fact,
a soot sprite, is what greeted me when I entered the transporter room.

Encore, Part III - How Ya Livin'? (What?) How Ya Livin'? (What?)

40 visits done and radiation completed. On my last day, I clanged the bell in the lobby. They want you to ceremoniously ring this bell three times, in recognition of your treatment being done. I wasn't going to do it, but I eventually relented, and it was pretty fun after all, even though there's a typo on the brass plaque under the bell, which drove me crazy.

I waited six weeks, as instructed, and I got yet another PSA test. At this point, since I was already missing my prostate, I figured my PSA was supposed to be undetectable.

It was 0.6.

To review: first it was 33 (29!), then zero, then 0.2, then 0.2 again, then 0.4. Then I had radiation, and it rose to 0.6. The big fancy beast machine had not done its job by killing the microscopic "cancer you have," after all. If anything, it seemed to have encouraged a higher PSA and created more cancer, and I wondered if the radiation gang had the big fancy machine set on reverse, by mistake. On my very last treatment day, one of them had joked, "Okay, we've had 39 practice runs, today we're finally going to turn the beam on for the first time!" It seemed a lot less funny, upon hearing the results of the 40 visits.

Worse yet - no superpowers. I was still the same ordinary guitar player I was before.

Apparently, I was not cured.

Again.

A-hoo. Werewolves. Of London.

My radiation oncologist was not happy about this. I can see why - I was a blight on his otherwise excellent record. He told me that this is rare, but he has seen it before, and I couldn't help but think, "Typical me, always looking for attention by eating a cigarette, or not getting cured with radiation..." He used the phrase "doggone it" twice in our post-treatment consultation, and said I was "one of the good ones," which is what people say about somebody who they like, and has died, or is about to die, earlier than expected.

He also said that, once in a blue moon, as the last bundle of cancer cells die, they release some PSA, as a parting shot. And I thought, "Goddammit, Ghost Clint! Haven't you caused enough trouble?" That's what I get for creating the character in the first place. Now he's Undead Zombie Clint, and he's even more angry about his lawn.

After considering this sugar-coated optimism about the last, desperate spurt of PSA from the irradiated cancer cells, I thought a more likely scenario was that the stray cancer cells had purchased a summer home somewhere in my lymph system or skeleton, and were taking up permanent residence there. I thought about the stray shoots of grass I was digging up (merely stepping!) a year ago, the day after my surgery. I thought about how the new shoots were coming from a hidden underground root system, and how the elusive family of cancer cells was pretty similar.

Undead Zombie Clint: "Look here, we've got to find ourselves a new neighborhood - this one's all burned up from that big radiation storm a couple weeks ago. Plus, the plumbing's back to leaking, and it doesn't empty out all the way. Maybe we can get FEMA to set us up with a double-wide over in Lymphville. I hear they've got a new Cracker Barrel over there."

Mrs. Undead Zombie Clint: "C'mon, Junior, we're moving to Lymphville."

Clint, Junior: "OMG, I hate you both. All my friends are here." <commences sulking>

And now they were going to be even harder to locate, since they had turned off the GPS tracking on their flip-phones, and were riding dirty. They had expired driver's licenses, they were wanted for parole violation and radiation dodging, and they were still unkempt and disrespectful.

Now, in a subsequent visit to my urologist/surgeon, I learned a few other tidbits of information. For example, radiation takes 18 months to completely work. It's not like the smoke clears, the sheriff twirls his gun, and everything that's supposed to be dead is dead. In the post-apocalyptic ruin that is your prostate bed, things will be settling, and dying, for a long while.

Speaking of being dead, radiation treatments actually destroy your DNA in the target area. Cells can't even properly reproduce or behave normally for a while. Absorb the gravity of that - your DNA is destroyed. So, all bets are off, when it comes to the recovery of the damaged neighborhood. It might take a minute, and any test results might be slightly unreliable.

Oh, that whole business about PSA rising because Undead Zombie Clint hurled a last parting shot? Turns out that's a real thing. It's called PSA Bounce, and science is still somewhat baffled by it. Up it goes, then it comes back down, and nobody is exactly sure why. You have to wait.

Longer than you want to. By a lot. Like, PSA bounce can happen two years after radiation is completed. Patience, Grasshopper. Patience.

Here's a late-breaking development - turns out there's a fancy new scan that's even better than the Axumin. Turns out it's available in Europe. Turns out it's not available in America.

Or is it?

Well, now it is. It wasn't when I first wrote this section, but it has since become available at a place in Los Angeles. So, I was thinking about heading to L.A. to get myself a fancy new PSMA (prostate-specific membrane antigen) scan, if my PSA continued to rise.

And now I don't have to go to L.A. Because, by the time I got around to rewriting the next section, it had become available right here in Las Vegas.

I had been cheerfully told by my radiation oncologist that radiation treatments usually result in a lifespan "measured in years, not weeks or months." This is meant to reassure patients who fear that they only have a weekend to get their affairs in order, before turning in their room key and checking out permanently from the Mortal Coil Hotel. Furthermore, the lifespan being narrated to me was, "five, ten...I once had a patient that lived another twelve years." And this did not meet with my approval at all. I had another thirty-seven years in mind, thank you very much. Well, if I hadn't already made a Rolling Stones reference earlier, I would say, "You can't always get what you want." But one Stones reference is enough.

What happens next, if you're in this situation? Same thing that always happens next - you wait a few months, then you get another PSA test. And then another. And then another, until some sort of pattern can be established. And you hope for a number that falls, or at least doesn't go up by a magnitude. My radiation oncologist had said that, once in a great while, in this situation, the PSA eventually starts drifting downward, like it's supposed to, and you're in the clear. Is this narrative a fantasy, designed mostly to sugar-coat the bad news and let the patient down easy? Or is it a legit, realistic expectation? Time will tell.

Sometimes, time tells faster than you think it will. Three months after my 0.6 PSA test, I scored another 0.6. I took it as a victory. But three months after that, I scored an impressive 0.9. My family of cells has almost certainly moved to Lymphville or Bonestown. This is not ideal. But here we are.

Well, if anybody thinks I'm going to quietly be a "cancer patient" and slowly coast over the finish line, you can think again, mister! I've got chains to yank, guitars to play at high volume, and speed limits to break. There are plenty of new experiences out there for me, which will sometimes delight, sometimes disappoint, and sometimes scare, and that's the way it should be. Besides, as a friend of mine once said, "You never feel so alive as when you're scared to death." So, I'm going to see how many more questionable choices I can make before I'm through. If it turns out that I'm on the five-to-ten-year plan, it means I have a lot of tomfoolery to cram into a short period of time.

If experience has taught me nothing else, it's that there is no permanent guarantee. But for now, I'm living to be 100. Even if I only live to be 70.

Clanging the ceremonial bell, after completing
40 blasts of radiation.

This Is The End

(for real this time)

Undead Zombie Clint has caused a ruckus. And now I'm about to embark on an exciting ride on the Hormone Express.

Oo, the Hogwarts Express!

No, Hormone!

Oo, Hermione, from the Harry Potter movies!

No, HORMONE! Pay attention, nerd boy!

Some guys don't tolerate this hormone stuff very well, but believe me when I tell you that I'm committed to taking enough androgen suppressant to turn me into a fully-engineered Trans woman. I once ate a cigarette, you know. You can't scare me.

Apparently, there are also a couple of new cancer drugs that were developed just in the last couple of years. I guess scientists came up with these new therapies in their spare time, when they weren't battling covid and enduring the ignorance of the general public. I'll probably be trying those when my medical people say it's time. But never mind all that. That's for later, and this is now.

Robot assisted radical prostatectomy worked. Then, when it was no longer working, radiation was tried, and it didn't work. So, you try the next thing. And medical science keeps you going, until it can't.

I could go on writing this "encore" for the rest of my life, however long that ends up being, and I really wanted to draw the line at the end of chapter 31. But the audience gave a standing ovation (or so I imagine, with my overactive imagination), and in traditional show biz style, I saved a reasonably amusing radiation story for the very end. You know, if you're Frank Sinatra, you don't sing *My Way* in the regular set, you save it for the encore. That's right, I've just compared myself to Sinatra, which is a clear indicator that I should step away from the computer keyboard and shut up.

CURTAIN CALL

Thank you for coming to the show, and staying for the three-part encore. Let's hear it for the crew! They're the best, and they're all working their asses off to save our lives, or at least make our lives a bit longer. The box office people and ushers do a great job of scheduling us and getting us all where we need to go. The marketing and promotion team make sure we all know that the show exists, and tell us where and when the show is. And the financial department handles all of our medical insurance complexity.

The gang in the lighting booth runs the 2.2 million dollar linear accelerator machine, and all the various scanners that find unauthorized cells inside of us. Backstage, the deck crew is wheeling us to the operating theater, changing the sheets on our hospital beds, and holding a flashlight for us when we can't see our way to the stage. The wardrobe department provides us with air-conditioned gowns! The riggers install green lasers in the ceiling to locate our jailhouse tattoos. And the audio team plays *Star Trek* theme songs through the overhead speakers. The directors give us valuable guidance and insight, and the special effects team creates very realistic blood and surgery effects. We couldn't have done the show without the fantastic crew. Thanks, gang.

But most of all, let's hear it for the cast. That's you and me, champions. We get fingered, scanned, tested, and evaluated. We get categorized with numbers. We go under the knife and get things cut out of us. We recover, struggle, fail and triumph, all while being observed by an audience of medical people, friends, family, and total strangers. We are elated and disappointed, sometimes in a very short space of time. And time is what this show is all about, after all. With a little luck, and with a lot of skill, our time gets a little longer. Maybe we get to do an encore.

We decorate the world with our personalities for as long as we can, and we are members of the cast for as long as our show runs. One day the show will close. But not today.

Thank you all, and good night.

CLOSING CREDITS

I've used a lot of sarcasm and smart-alecky attitude in this story, but the reason I'm still currently alive to tell it is because of a number of dedicated professionals. These people put up with a lot of nonsense from patients like me - patients who think they're clever, unique, the life of the party, the most fun patient ever to come into the office, the most well-adjusted, the happiest. Some of us try way too hard at these titles, and end up looking and acting the fool. I am the poster child for this behavior. Thank goodness for the professionals, who put up with us.

The Professionals

The Urologist, The Surgeon: Dr. Omid Alex Lesani

The Radiation Oncologist: Dr. Douglas R. Debenham

The Finger: Dr. Haibin Zhang

The Bone Scan Operator: Kristie

The Axumin Scan Operator: Jason

Elite CT Scan Team #1: (...names withheld for legal reasons)

The Radiation Technicians: Andrew, Kris, Tracey

The Scheduler: Zsuzsanna

The Fixer: Robert

The HPA: Ari

The Daytime Nurse: Leroy

Drain Hose Queen: "Serena" (I never got her real name)

The Starbucks Barista In Nursing School: Emily

Thanks to Connie Corrick, Annette Verdolino, and Cathy Wilson, who all proofread this thing and pointed out all of my sloppy spelling and grammar. As another friend of mine likes to say, "Look, I'm a writer, not an editor!" Annette also did the awesome graphic design, and made my little storybook look like an actual professional product.

Genuine thanks to everybody who bought this book. I hope you liked it. If you're "one of the cast," I hope you beat cancer. If you're an industry professional, you have my undying respect. If you're someone who has lost a loved one to prostate cancer, you have my heartfelt sympathy. If you're a young person in med school, thank goodness you've come along. Go forward and cure people.

Now, everybody go home. We've got to clean the theater. Y'all made a mess up in here.

The Musical!

(It's not.)

Gonna buy 5 copies for my mother - Cover Of The Rolling Stone (Doctor Hook and the Medicine Show)

Werewolves Of London - Werewolves Of London (Warren Zevon)

Nothing bad ever happens to me - Nothing Bad Ever Happens To Me (Oingo Boingo)

Sign, Sign, Everywhere A Sign - Signs (The Five Man Electrical Band)

Somebody Get Me A Doctor - Somebody Get Me A Doctor (Van Halen)

Doctor Please, Some More Of These - Mother's Little Helper (The Rolling Stones)

Gonna Use My Fingers - Brass In Pocket (The Pretenders)

Check Baby, Check Baby, 1, 2, 3, 4... - Rump Shaker (Wreckx-N-Effect)

You Let Me Violate You - Closer (Nine Inch Nails)

Rico Suave - Rico Suave (Gerardo)

I Got The News - I Got The News (Steely Dan)

I haven't got time for the pain - Haven't Got Time For The Pain (Carly Simon)

Come Up To The Lab And See What's On The Slab - Sweet Transvestite (Rocky Horror Picture Show)

The Waiting Is The Hardest Part - The Waiting (Tom Petty)

Hangin' On The Telephone - Hangin' On The Telephone (Blondie)

Devil Inside - Devil Inside (INXS)

Cuts Like A Knife - Cuts Like A Knife (Bryan Adams)

It's Showtime! Showtime! - 24 Karat Magic (Bruno Mars)

Wake Up, Little Suzy - Wake Up, Little Suzy (The Everly Brothers)

Get Up, Stand Up - Get Up, Stand Up (Bob Marley and the Wailers)

Day After Day - Day After Day (Badfinger) or...

Day After Day - Day After Day (Men At Work) Reader's choice on this one.

Ain't nothin' gonna break-a my stride, ain't nothin' gonna slow me down - Break My Stride (Matthew Wilder)

Homeward Bound - Homeward Bound (Simon and Garfunkel)

Gimme Three Steps - Gimme Three Steps (Lynrd Skynrd)

Let's Get It Started - Let's Get It Started (Black Eyed Peas)

When The Levee Breaks - When The Levee Breaks (Led Zeppelin)

They Try To Make Me Go To Rehab - Rehab (Amy Winehouse)

Doctor Doctor, Gimme The News - Bad Case Of Loving You (Robert Palmer)

Poor Little Fool - Poor Little Fool (Ricky Nelson)

Big Ten Inch - Big Ten Inch Record (Aerosmith)

The Harder They Come - The Harder They Come (Jimmy Cliff)

back up in the game, runnin' fast to take my swing - Return Of The Mack (Mark Morrison)

River Of Dreams - River Of Dreams (Billy Joel)

A Whole New World - A Whole New World (from Disney's Aladdin soundtrack)

Mama's Got A Squeeze Box - Squeeze Box (The Who)

Oh Kegel, Kegel, Kegel... - inspired by The Dreidel Song, English version by Samuel E. Goldfarb, Yiddish version by Mikhl Gelbart

Born To Be Wild - Born To Be Wild (Steppenwolf)

Dare To Be Stupid - Dare To Be Stupid ("Weird Al" Yankovic)

Further On Up The Road - Further On Up The Road (originally by Bobby "Blue" Bland, in this case I'm thinking of the version by Eric Clapton)

Guess Who's Back...Back Again... - Without Me (Eminem)

<u>Just A Song Before I Go</u> - Just A Song Before I Go (Crosby, Stills, And Nash)

<u>Carry On, Wayward Son</u> - Carry On Wayward Son (Kansas)

<u>Fade Away And Radiate</u> - Fade Away And Radiate (Blondie)

<u>Energized</u> - It's an album title by Foghat, not a song. But I really needed it for this section heading.

<u>How Ya Livin'? (What?) How Ya Livin'? (What?)</u> - Theme song from In Living Color (season 3 version)

<u>You can't always get what you want</u> - You Can't Always Get What You Want (The Rolling Stones)

<u>This Is The End</u> - The End (The Doors)

CPSIA information can be obtained
at www.ICGtesting.com
Printed in the USA
BVHW081134300123
657433BV00006B/139